Geoff Tristram has been a pro
over thirty years, working for a
Penguin, Embassy World Snook
Past Times, Ravensburger Puzzl
Pursuit and the television show,   ... Over!', to
name but a few.

He has created artwork featuring the likes of Jonathan Ross,
Jeremy Clarkson, Ian Botham, David Vine, Steve Bull, Alan
Shearer, Ian Hislop and Gary Lineker, not to mention virtually
every famous snooker player that ever lifted a cue. You may have
even noticed him at the Crucible World Championships on TV,
interviewing them as he drew their caricatures!

He has also designed many book covers, album sleeves for
bands such as *UB40*, *The Maisonettes* and *City Boy* (remember
them?), and postage stamps, notably 'Charles and Diana – The
Royal Wedding', 'Miss World', 'Lake Placid Winter Olympics'
and 'Spain 1982 World Cup Football'.

More recently, his incredibly detailed 'Cat Conundrum' puzzle
paintings have enthralled and exasperated thousands of dedicated
puzzle-solvers all over the world.

Geoff's younger brother, David, is a well known and extremely
successful comedy playwright, so it was no real surprise when
Geoff eventually turned his hand to comedy writing, hence this,
his eighth full-length novel, the second outing for his new comic
creation, the chaotic and obsessive writer, Adam Eve.

In order to make up for lost time, Geoff has recently finished
his ninth book, a prequel to his first ever story, 'A Nasty Bump on
the Head', featuring the delightfully scatterbrained and dreamy
young artist, David Day (aged ten and a half).

Having been forced to purchase a block of ten ISBNs at the cost
of £70 (you can't purchase them singly), it is a safe bet that at least
one more Adam Eve book will follow in due course, before Geoff
retires from public life.

Mr Maori Goes Home

Geoff Tristram

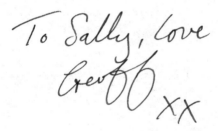

To Sally, love
Geoff
xx

**DRAWING
ROOM**

First published in 2009 by The Drawing Room Press.

Printed and bound by CPI Group (UK) Ltd, Croydon, CR0 4YY

and in New Zealand by Bookprinting.co.nz Auckland

ISBN 978-0-9551428-8-8

Thank you to Laura Tristram for weeding out most, if not all of the typos, which I plant on purpose just to test her superb editing skills.

Cover illustration by Geoff Tristram

Contact the author on gt@geofftristram.co.uk

For 'Hurricane' Kimmy,
who flew 12,000 miles to watch a *Split Enz* concert
in Auckland, New Zealand,
and then flew home again the next day.

What a girl!

No possums were harmed in the writing of this book.

I can't tell you how delighted I was when I read that Martin Clunes had filmed a one-off television drama about an Englishman who is charged with the task of returning a precious Maori carving to a small museum New Zealand. Once my wife had coaxed me down from the roof and hidden all the kitchen knives and aspirin tablets, I desperately began searching for the silver lining. I nervously watched this cursed programme through the fingers of my left hand, taking fortifying gulps of Shiraz with my right one. (Okay, I realize you can't gulp with a right hand. Stop being so pedantic. Can't you see I'm suffering here?) And do you know what? I came out of it with my head held high. I won't say I was as happy as Larry. For a start, the Larry I know isn't that happy. It goes without saying that in an ideal world I would have preferred there not to be another story sharing such an odd and unlikely premise, but that's life. It is seldom perfect. Great minds think alike, and all that.

The good news – for me more than Martin I have to say – is that for all the lavish locations, the swanky script-writers, expensive film crews, famous actors and what-have-you, my version is still, conservatively, around ten times better and funnier. Okay, that might not sound too modest, but it's true, and I swear on my mother's life, it was a complete coincidence, as a lot of things are in my world. I got *my* idea from a comical, accident-filled holiday in New Zealand, coupled with the recently unearthed history of a dodgy carving that resides in the Maori café in Kinver, near to where I live. I just feel sorry for Martin Clunes. If only he'd read my book first, I feel sure he'd never have agreed to film the other version.

Anyway, never mind eh? I've already erased it from my mind, and begun working on my next masterpiece. It's about a cultured but insane Russian doctor who eats bits of his victims and ends up in a secure unit wearing a mask. I wrote it while snacking on fava beans and sipping a good Chianti.

Geoff Tristram

CHAPTER 1

In which I have a strange dream, followed by some very bad news and some very good news, albeit with a catch.

Paul McCartney had dropped in at the small pub where my band and I were playing, as he'd often promised to do, and offered to sing a couple of numbers with us. We knew *Get Back* and *Hey Jude* fairly well, and he said he did too, so we agreed on those. Then I realized that one of the strap screws on my Les Paul was missing, so that I couldn't hang the guitar around my neck. Frustrated beyond belief, I begged Paul to be patient, bought him a lager, and hot-footed it next-door to the little music shop, to discover that the wizened old fellow with smeared spectacles and unkempt hair who ran the place was just about to lock up for the night. I begged him for help, acutely aware that people of McCartney's reputation wouldn't wait around forever in a smoky bar for the promise of a jam session, even if it was with an old mate. The doddery old fool went about his task like one of those Galapagos Island turtles (and a particularly dozy one at that), dithering around and muttering to himself as he searched high and low for some old plastic box full of guitar bits.

'What type of guitar did you say it was again?' he mumbled.

'A Gibson Les Paul Standard,' I repeated, drumming my fingers nervously on his counter and breathing with some difficulty, as if my first coronary were imminent.

'Any idea of the year?' he asked slowly. 'They changed the design after—'

1

'I couldn't bloody care less about the design,' I interrupted, somewhat tetchily, 'just find me any old bloody strap screw that'll screw into a lump of mahogany and I'll be out of your hair. At this juncture, I don't care if it's a brass cup hook.'

His telephone rang, and he excused himself in order to answer it. It was his wife, asking him what he wanted for his dinner when he got home. I can't remember what he said he fancied offhand, because I was wound up like a coiled spring, a bag of nerves. It was the biggest moment of my musical life and I was about to blow it. I took it upon myself to ransack his drawers and empty them onto his counter, such was my impatience. Tiny springs, plectrums, volume knobs and the like, showered down like rain, clattering off his work-surface and cascading onto the floor. The old duffer shouted angrily for me to cease, replaced his receiver and began his epic journey from the back office to where I stood rummaging furiously. He was interrupted by the phone once more, but strangely, this time it sounded as if it were strapped to my right ear, such was the volume and intensity of its ring. I sat bolt upright, gasping for breath, and realized that it was the extension phone next to my bed that was doing the ringing. I yanked the receiver off the wall, tearing away the body of the phone and two dusty rawlplugs in the process, and croaked, 'Hello?', but no one replied. At least, no one human. I did just about hear what sounded like a chipmunk trapped deep inside one of my bedside lockers, but I put this down to early morning delirium. Then I realized that I was holding the phone upside down, so I turned it around and tried again. This time I was answered by a female voice. I say female, it was actually my Aunt Mavis who is borderline, but I won't go into that right now. She's been divorced from my Uncle Ken for ages, and the news that she was about to impart made any chance of a reconciliation unlikely. Uncle Ken, she informed me rather matter-of-factly, had shuffled off his mortal coil, which was always on the cards, given his lifestyle, and he had 'remembered' me in his will, as I believe the expression is. To clarify things, I'm talking about Wild Uncle Ken from Devon, not my Uncle Jim – the one that was murdered by the psychopathic locksmith who

2

stabbed him and rammed a pantomime horse's rubber hoof down his throat because he had mistaken him for me.

In spite of the fact that I was three-parts comatose and extremely disorientated after yet another of my frustration dreams, I was quite upset. Ken and I weren't super-close, if you know what I mean, but he was good company, possibly because you never quite knew what he would do next. They say that opposites attract, and so it was with us. I am, or at least was at that time, a bit of a low-key home bird, whereas he lived his life pretty much along the lines of Keith Richards, with elements of Richard Harris, Peter O'Toole and Oliver Reed thrown in for good measure. He had once been in the merchant navy and travelled the world, wreaking havoc in every port, whereas a crazy night out for me was having a second glass of Shiraz and staying awake for the duration of the nine o'clock film on channel four.

Anyway, Aunt Mavis didn't seem overly bothered, as she had remarried, hadn't seen him for ten years or more and hadn't been left a penny. She did however feel duty-bound to keep me abreast, albeit nearly a week late, for which she apologized profusely. She'd been on holiday abroad, she explained, and only found out when she returned. She wished me well, adding that being 'remembered' in a will didn't mean that I could necessarily order my first Ferrari. I assured her that I understood entirely, and was quite impressed that Ken was capable of remembering anything, let alone me in his will, given his lifestyle. It was, she continued, the booze that had done for him. In his defence, Ken had always tried to adhere to the government guidelines on alcohol consumption, and more or less stuck to his twenty-one units per night. Imagine his dismay when he discovered, after thirty years of careful monitoring, that the recommended amount was in fact intended to last him the whole week. I suppose Ken's vision was probably too blurred to ever read the fine detail in the leaflet, come to think about it.

But I'm forgetting my manners.

3

Don't you love those corny James Bond-type films where the evil villain sits in a black leather chair, stroking a fluffy cat, with a huge scar down his cheek? – the villain has the scar I mean, not the cat, but I suppose the cat could be evil and have a scar too, and he – the villain, not the cat, always says something along the lines of:

'But I'm forgetting my manners, Mr Bond; my name is Charles Masterson, but you may know me better as Doctor Death.'

Where was I? I've lost the thread now. Oh yes, but I'm forgetting my manners, my name is Adam – and we may as well get this over with straight away – my surname is Eve. It's a long story best not gone into here, but suffice it to say that it was my mother's fault. Apparently, she never realized how stupid it sounded until the vicar was splashing water all over me at the font and her relatives were sniggering in the aisles. I am now a member of that elite group of people with idiotic names; people such as Chris Packet, Tania Bottom and Annette Kertin, to name but three. I'm a professional writer by trade, which always sounds grand, but trust me, it isn't. I've had a couple of novels published that didn't exactly set the world on fire, and to make ends meet, I write mildly amusing articles for a few newspapers and magazines – mainly the ones where grammar isn't an issue and there are always a pair of pneumatic breasts on the opposite page to make sure you never read the article anyway. I'm a thirty-seven–year-old heterosexual with an ex-wife and two kids, one of each, and I have recently parted company with a very nice school teacher lady named – and just what are the odds of this happening? – Eve Adams, that I met a year or so ago, just after she'd returned her pantomime horse to the fancy dress shop. (I'd returned *my* pantomime horse the week before, so already we had something in common.) She had been offered a dream job as the headmistress of a New England school that she desperately wanted to accept, and I was petrified of long-haul flights and just didn't want to live in America, so that, sadly, was the end of that. I was all on my own again.

4

Physically, I'm told that I resemble Nicholas Cage and a young Eric Sykes in equal measure. This is a little like saying that someone looks like a cross between Steve McQueen and the Queen Mother. I will never understand how it can be possible to combine both, but that is what they say and I have to believe them, like it or not. I think it's probably the way I talk that reminds them of Eric. At least, I hope it is. Thankfully, at least, none of my movies have been complete turkeys, unlike Nicholas Cage's, and that's because I've never made any. A bit of a negative way of safeguarding against it I admit, but one hundred per cent effective. Do nothing with your life and you won't make any mistakes, I always say; apart from the colossal mistake of doing absolutely nothing with your life, that is.

Once I'd said goodbye to Aunt Mavis, I staggered downstairs to make breakfast and get cracking on a fascinating article I was writing for the Stourbridge News about why women feel the need to paint their toenails. I live on my own in a small apartment near Stourbridge in the West Midlands, and have done ever since my wife, Katie, decided to leave me but keep the big detached house and my children. Incidentally, that reminds me – I must send her solicitor a nice card some day to thank her for that.

I put the kettle on and riffled through the mail, which was mainly bills and junk, as usual. There was, however, one letter, franked with the company name 'Norfolk and Chance' – I kid you not – which looked a bit official, and so it turned out to be. They were my uncle's solicitors, and they'd wasted no time whatsoever in writing to me to tell me about his will, and my inclusion in it. The senior partner, a Mr Edward Chance, was asking me to ring him as soon as possible for some reason, which sounded quite exciting. I recalled Mavis's warning about not counting my chickens (or, for that matter, my Ferraris), took a deep breath and rang the number. A receptionist with an awful, phoney telephone voice that reminded me, for some strange reason, of a bumble bee trapped under a glass, asked my business and put me straight through. Mr Chance wished me good morning and expressed his sympathy. I responded with my standard 'sad' voice – the one newscasters switch to when they have to deal with a tragic piece straight after a light-hearted one. You know the kind of thing.

'Percy the Skate-Boarding Chicken has just entered the Guinness Book of Records as the first skate-boarding chicken to travel a hundred metres in under two minutes. *And in Bangladesh, news that seventy-five million people lost their lives today when a mountain range fell on top of them.*'

Mr Chance asked if we were close (me and Uncle Ken I mean, not me and Mr Chance), and I replied, rather dimwittedly, that we were and we weren't. Whenever we met, which wasn't as often in recent years due to his move down to Devon, we always got on really well. He made me laugh with his cavalier attitude to life, and teased me about not living my own life to the full, which was true – I didn't. I suppose I was a bit like the son he never had, come to think of it. Mind you, I wouldn't have wanted him for a father. My dad is a lovely, quiet, suburban, gentle sort of chap, and that's what you need for a dad. Lord knows why his brother turned out completely the opposite. Perhaps my grandmother was having an affair with Lord Byron while granddad was at work, and Ken was the result. He certainly wasn't from the same gene pool that my dad paddled around in, that's for sure. The quiet life didn't appeal to Ken, and he was always criticizing me in a jokey way for inventing all sorts of crazy adventures for the heroes of my novels to experience, but not living life to the full myself. In my defence, I would explain to him that, whilst the exploits of Richard Harris or Peter O'Toole might make amusing reading in someone's memoirs, often their actions impacted on other people – wives, children and so on. Besides, I liked my creature comforts. I didn't fancy popping out for a quiet drink on a Friday night and then waking up in a brothel in Malta with millions of badly-done tattoos, a full beard, ragged clothing and complete memory loss. I'd allow the characters in my comedy novels do that, but it wasn't for me, thank you.

Mr Chance listened politely to my thorough fifteen minute answer to his initial enquiry (which was, in case you've forgotten, 'were Ken and I close?'), and was probably wishing he'd never asked. He spotted a gap and quickly got down to the nitty-gritty, before I had chance to wax lyrical about anything else. Uncle Ken, it turned out, was a dark horse, financially speaking, and this came as a complete surprise to me. It appears that the old devil had bunged his last tenner on the National Lottery in March 2003 whilst inebriated, and belatedly discovered that he'd won a fair old sum the week after, when he visited a lap dancing emporium in Plymouth. Grubbing around in his trousers for a fiver, he accidentally pulled out the winning ticket and slipped it under his private dancer's garter belt. It was only when she gave him a good slap and demanded cash instead that he realized his mistake, duly paid the woman and simultaneously retrieved his million pound ticket from between her legs. I presume that this slapper never found out what she had parted with in return for her paltry fiver. Mr Chance went on to explain that since the big payday, Ken had selflessly dedicated himself to converting his windfall into champagne, with the result that neither his body nor his bank balance was as healthy as they had been. That said, there was still just over a quarter of a million left after legal fees, with no children to leave it to, and in Ken's own words, the bitch Mavis wasn't going to benefit, so that just left his brother (my father), and my brother and sister, who had been left sixty thousand between them, and his favourite nephew, Adam, who was to get the rest.

Well, as you can imagine, this all came as a bit of a shock. I could see at least two telephones dancing before me, and I had to clutch the breakfast table to stop me slithering down onto the floor. My recently deceased Uncle Jim had also seen fit to bequeath me a decent sum only the previous year, you see. It had come in very handy at a time when I was, quite frankly, on what is oft referred to as the bones of one's arse, but this latest donation was in a different league altogether. I must admit, it all seemed very unfair to me, even though it was biased in my favour. Maybe

7

Ken thought dad wasn't in need of too much money, and figured that Steve, being a well-known playwright, was quite well-off. He never really got to know the youngest sibling, Evelyn, for whatever reason, so maybe that coloured his decision there. Still, twenty grand was a lot better than a poke in the eye with a billiard cue. I just hoped that my getting the lion's share wouldn't cause problems with the others.

'You did just say two hundred thousand pounds, *after* solicitor's fees?' I queried. It wouldn't quite sink in, you see.

'Correct!' Mr Chance assured me. 'His flat was rented, so there's no property, and his possessions are only fit for the skip, with maybe one exception.'

'And I can just pop in to see you and, erm, collect this huge sum?' I drooled.

'Ah!' said Mr Chance. 'It's not that simple. There was, let us say, a condition attached.'

'I knew there would be,' I sighed. 'Do tell.'

'Well, it's all rather peculiar really. As you know, our Mr Kenneth Eve used to be in the merchant navy, and travelled the world.'

I confirmed this. He had tried to rape and pillage most of it too, if Mavis was to be believed.

'It appears that, during a visit to Rotorua in New Zealand, some thirty-odd years ago, he stole a very rare and valuable Maori carving from the museum there, presumably after a night of what used to be called high jinx. When dictating his will, he explained to me that he has always felt a sense of deep guilt over this foolhardy act, and his dying wish was that it should be returned.'

'I should think so,' I replied, for I take a dim view of theft, and for that matter, any illegal activity, no matter how pleasurable.

'So why don't we arrange for a courier firm to deliver it back to this Maori museum? *If* it's true that I've inherited all this money – and I'm still half-expecting to wake up frustrated at any minute and realize that the Paul McCartney sequence wasn't actually the end of my dream – I will gladly pay for this to be done out of my winnings.'

Mr Chance sucked his tooth in what sounded like a contemplative and troubled way.

'Setting to one side for a moment your comment about Paul McCartney, which I confess has taken me into dark and unfathomable waters, I am afraid that Uncle Ken insisted that this was not an option. He was quite specific.'

'Specific about what?' I asked.

'He insisted that, in order for you to claim your inheritance, you must *personally* deliver the Maori carving to the museum.'

'But why?' I groaned. 'I mean, it's not like I'm ungrateful, he's left me a bloody fortune after all, but I'm absolutely petrified of flying, and New Zealand is a bloody long way, apparently.'

'You are not wrong there. It takes twenty-four hours in one go, unless you choose to break the journey up by staying in, say, Singapore for a day. It is so far away that if it were any further away, it would, in fact, be closer.'

I stared incredulously at the receiver. Mr Chance had obviously been at the drink, and before the sun had gone over the yard arm too, whatever that was.

'I'm sorry?'

'It's as far away as it is possible to get from England. If it were any further away, it would be closer to us if we travelled around the world in the other direction.'

Well, this was marvellous news. I hated flying even short distances and got all panicky just thinking about it. Italy or Spain I could just about cope with, so long as I'd swallowed a few of those mini-bottles of wine that they supplied with your in-flight dinner, but this was different. Twenty-four hours – a complete day and night at thirty-five thousand feet. It just wasn't natural. The engines might seize up with all that effort. I just couldn't do it. I was unwilling, and I told Mr Chance so in no uncertain terms.

'Then I'm afraid you won't be able to claim your inheritance,' he informed me sadly. 'This is a legal document, and Ken insisted that his wishes were carried out to the letter.'

'But that's madness,' I replied wearily. 'These art couriers are trained to carry important paintings around the world. How do you think Picassos are ferried about? Not by Picasso's bloody nephews, that's for sure. They use proper people with padded boxes and security and so on. I'm such an idiot; I'd probably drop it and break its head off or something – if it's got a head. Can't we cheat, and I'll pay for it to be sent by Christie's or whoever?'

'No.'

'What if I gave you loads of money to turn a blind eye?'

'Sorry.'

'And did the silly bugger explain to you why he wanted me to do this personally?'

'Yes.'

'So can you explain it to me?'

'No.'

There was more, but that, in a nutshell, was the gist of our conversation. I arranged to visit Mr Chance at his offices as soon as was possible, where I was to collect the Maori carving, an object that I had already developed an irrational hatred of. I even asked, cheekily I thought, if anyone could actually prove whether I had made the trip in person or just hired Alan Whicker to deliver it in return for a couple of grand. The bad news was, Ken, the

10

scheming dead bastard, had even thought of that, and I had to supply a clear photo of myself standing outside the Maori Museum before Norfolk and Chance would release the funds. I had no idea why my uncle would subject me to this, knowing full-well how I disliked long distance travel. He probably dreamt the idea up while he was three sheets to the wind and sharing a bed with at least a dozen hookers. 'I only have dull old Adam to leave it to, but I'm going to make him suffer!' he probably thought to himself, as he snorted his umpteenth line of coke.

They say that travel broadens the mind, but I've never been keen on it, even when I was younger. Besides, why would I need to broaden my mind? I was always pretty broad-minded anyway. I never batted an eyelid when my own solicitor turned into a woman, halfway through my litigation case with a publishing company – I won't name names, just in case they read my books. They certainly didn't when *they* were publishing them, that's for sure.

Anyway, to cut a long story short, and many would argue that it's already too late for that, we'd been plugging away at them, my solicitor, James, and I, and I was kind of hoping I'd get my settlement by Christmas, as I was a bit short. I received a letter on the 20th of December from my solicitor's offices, but the purpose of it was to inform me that, from the 5th of January, their copyright lawyer, James Pirbright, wished to be known as Nina Williams. Well, I have to admit that I didn't see that one coming.

They say that hindsight's a wonderful thing, but I suppose, had I been a little more observant, I should have known. Old James had longish hair for a thirty-year-old solicitor, but it was manly long hair, like he might have played in a rock band at weekends; it wasn't all bouffanty and precious like a woman's. I did notice that his eyebrows seemed a bit too neat and plucked, but I put that down to him maybe being cursed with a mono-brow that he couldn't live with, rather than anything weirder. It was all rather odd, I have to admit, but I'm the sort of chap who can deal with a shock very quickly and be back on an even keel within no time. If

11

I woke up in the middle of the night and there was, for the sake of argument, say, a bat flitting around my bedroom, it would obviously make me jump momentarily, but within seconds I'd have assessed the situation, calmed myself, cornered the thing with a tea towel and ushered it out of the nearest open window. That's how I would deal with a bat (not that I've ever had to; it was a hypothetical example), and that is also how I deal with transsexual solicitors. I exude nonchalance.

When my settlement finally did materialize, I simply strode into his / her office with a broad smile, proffered a hand and broke the ice instantly with a clever little line about not being sure whether we should be shaking hands or kissing cheeks. Old Nina was relieved, as it was her first day back after the Christmas break and it must have been awkward for her. She was wearing the full regalia too, coiffured hair, blouse, bra, skirt, high heels, Chanel No.5 and a trace of stubble. We laughed at my witticism, me in a manly baritone and she in a newly-acquired falsetto. Then we chatted about this and that like old pals for a good half-hour, and she eventually handed over my cheque.

So you see, I've always been a liberal, broadminded type. I've also always been completely scatterbrained, with the three second memory of a tadpole and I can't remember for the life of me where all this was leading.

Oh yes, travel broadens the mind, that's it. Okay, well the thing about travel, as I mentioned earlier, is that I was one of those who could take it or leave it. I just wasn't adventurous. I've never been the sort to jet off somewhere exotic in order to teach South American street orphans how to grow seeds or whatever. I've never had the slightest urge to trudge through acres of dense rainforest looking for rare bugs whilst getting bitten senseless by the less-rare ones. I can't see the percentage in living in a one man tent to avoid a wind-chill factor of minus sixty and watching my urine turn to icicles as it leaves me. I am very fond of my toes, each and every one, and the idea of them turning black and dropping off, along with my nose, is not one that sets me alight, and my opinion of flying is already well documented. The dilemma I faced reminded me of that silly game we used to play at school, the gist of which was, 'What would you do for a million pounds?'

Would you eat dog poo for a million pounds? Just half a teaspoonful and the million is yours. Would you suck a tramp's vomit through a sweaty sock? Drink a pint of pee? Kiss fat smelly Wendy from Class3?

Of course, it didn't matter what you replied, because no one had a million pounds to give you anyway. The difference was, a solicitor in Birmingham was now offering me real money – not a million I admit, but a substantial amount of money – to overcome one of my deep-rooted fears; the fear of the long-haul flight. I paced the room, tearing out clumps of hair that I could ill-afford to lose, while I weighed the pros and cons. I checked my diary to see if I could afford the time – I would need at least a month off work for starters. I studied my bank statements and blanched. It had not been one of my more successful years, work-wise. I poured a stiff Shiraz and ruminated. And then I decided.

I was going to New Zealand.

CHAPTER 2

In which I collect Mr Maori and get a surprise visit that I could have done without.

Dreams are funny things. I should have realized, when I was having my Paul McCartney one, that the old fool in the music shop was Syd Little, the thin, talentless individual with the huge pebble glasses from the so-called comedy partnership of Little and Large. That should have alerted me to the fact that it was but a dream, but it didn't. Even when he somehow morphed into my next-door neighbour near the end, it didn't dawn on me. Come to think of it, alarm bells should have sounded from the off, because I've just realized that the person I took for granted as being McCartney was in fact that dodgy antiques dealer, David Dickinson – the one with the creosoted face.

On that occasion, it was a music-themed frustration dream. In the past, it's usually been sexual. I'm always in some compromising situation or other with a red-hot girl who wants me carnally – why, I can't imagine – but I am constantly thwarted by the most ridiculous circumstances. Elderly relatives burst into bedrooms unannounced, my trousers won't open due to faulty zips – you name it, and sickeningly, the ending is always the same; I don't get to do the dirty deed. I'm sure a psychiatrist could set himself up for life with highly-paid lecture tours of the States, just by analysing my screwed-up mind and writing a paper on it.

Now, however, the irritating frustration dreams had been replaced by altogether more sinister nightmares and it didn't take Sherlock Holmes to figure out what had sparked those off. Since speaking to Mr Chance, I must have shot bolt upright in bed at least a dozen times, sweating like a glassblower's backside, fresh from a dream about a plane crash, or being eaten alive by Maori tribesmen, or some such nonsense. With all this going on in my head, it was hardly surprising that I hadn't given much thought to Uncle Ken, my sadistic benefactor, and all of a sudden I felt rather guilty. The reason he had purloined this carving in the first place would probably never be known, if in fact there was a reason, other than drunken devilment, but the guilt had obviously haunted him to his dying day. Maybe, in order to make peace with himself, he needed to have it delivered by a member of the Eve family to show a sort of corporate repentance.

Then I started to think a little more deeply. Why hadn't he asked my dad to deliver it? The old man might never see sixty again, but he was in relatively good nick and not too long in the tooth to cope with a trip down-under with my mother – not by a long chalk. The two brothers had never fallen out either, and were always laughing and joking when they occasionally met up. Why not give *me* twenty thousand, the same as my siblings, and my dad the lion's share? That seemed to be more like the correct pecking order to me, much as I was grateful for it being the other way round. That way, I'd get twenty thousand quid for doing bugger-all and dad could get rich and jetlagged instead. I thought about suggesting this to Mr Chance, but there was something about his manner; that Reginald Jeeves-style polite firmness of his, which told me instinctively not to bother. My words would surely have fallen on stony ground.

It was then, with a grim feeling of foreboding but also a blossoming sense of excitement, that I drove to Birmingham in my beaten up old MG Roadster and parked up on the forecourt of Norfolk and Chance's elegant Georgian offices. I was greeted by the secretary with the awful phoney voice, who took time off from

16

her filing – nails, that is, not paperwork – to inform Mr Chance of my arrival. Five minutes later, I was summoned to the inner sanctum, upstairs, first on the left.

Disappointingly, Mr Chance looked nothing like Reginald Jeeves. In fact, he was far more like Captain Mainwaring, but thinner, and around a foot taller. He asked me to sit down, buzzed Fiona (the phoney-voiced filer) for two cups of tea, and got down to it. From somewhere under his enormous desk he produced a cardboard box measuring approximately two feet by a foot. I was expecting something far bigger, unless of course he was just about to show me his new size fifteen Adidas trainers. He lifted the lid and extracted a lump of dark brown wood carved in the shape of a dumpy little warrior of sorts, with an angry mouth and two wild 'mother of pearl' eyes. There were lines cut into its body that I presumed represented those tattoos that Maoris always have, and he appeared not to be wearing anything to cover up his manhood. Either that or he was holding a boomerang at a strange angle, if indeed Maoris carry boomerangs. I may be confusing them with Aborigines.

'Well, here's the little fellow we spoke about,' smiled Mr Chance, handing him over to me for a closer look. 'We've christened him Mr Maori. He's not much to look at is he?'

I had to admit that I couldn't see anyone getting over-excited about getting him back, but then, we are all different and we all appreciate different things. How else could we explain Daniel O'Donnell?

'Well, it's the object in question all right,' continued the honest solicitor. 'We cleared the flat and there was only one Maori carving, so this is it, and it fits the description. Your uncle explained that it was an important religious piece dating back a couple of hundred years, and there were even articles in The Times about it back in the 1970s, when he took off with it. He was a bit of a devil, your uncle, wasn't he?'

I had to agree. Initially, I was puzzled as to why this was such a big deal to him, to the extent that he'd written it into his will, but I suppose, if one compared the item to art objects from European civilization, one could put his crime into context. I'm sure I would have felt equally guilt-ridden had I half-inched a small Vermeer from a gallery in Amsterdam. Then I panicked a little, as a thought flitted through my mind:

'You don't think I'd be liable for any criminal charges when I take it back, do you? You know, being a relative of his.'

'Absolutely not!' Mr Chance assured me. 'They'd welcome you like the Messiah I should imagine. Of course, it might not be a bad idea to keep it to yourself whilst you're over there. Don't advertise it, if you follow me, and if customs in New Zealand open your bags, you'll need a decent excuse. Other than that, have no fear. They can hardly jail you for the sins of an uncle!'

We talked about this and that for a while, and were just about wrapping it up when Fiona Phoney-Filer arrived with the tea. I thanked Mr Chance for his efforts and sat there, trying to drink my boiling hot tea ages after our conversation had run its course.

I don't know if this has ever happened to you, but companies that offer tea should ensure that it arrives at the beginning of the interview, not the end. It's dead embarrassing to sit there sipping away in silence, and you don't want to be churlish and leave it, after someone's made it for you. The small-talk became less and less frequent to the point where Mr Chance was pretending to look through his appointments diary, and I was blowing and sipping furiously at a tea mug the size of a small barrel, with the witty caption, 'Size *does* matter!' emblazoned on the side. I bet he'll rue the day he sent his dim-wit secretary out to buy the crockery, that's for sure. And then, he remembered something, so it all worked out for the best. Uncle Ken had also left me a box of 'stuff'. It was, according to Mr Chance, all useless, but either I took delivery or it went on the skip. He walked me downstairs, dragged a cardboard box from a broom closet and helped me to

18

the car with it. I dropped it into my tiny boot, wished him well, and drove back to Stourbridge to sort out my travel arrangements.

I parked on the multi-storey and stowed Mr Maori away in the boot alongside the box of Uncle Ken's bric-a-brac. I was paranoid about losing him now, or having him stolen. I took a quick peek at him before I closed the boot, as I hadn't really given him more than just a cursory glance in Mr Chance's office, but my initial opinion was not affected in any way. I still thought he was no more than an unimpressive, crudely carved lump. Mr Maori, in turn, seemed to be studying me with his evil mother of pearl stare, and no doubt came to exactly the same conclusion. I slammed the lid on him and descended the foul, urine-scented stairs to the high street.

Tina's Travel was empty, which was unusual, so I had the choice of three women to talk to, each sitting behind their neat light ash-effect desks wearing their smart blue uniforms. I instinctively chose the one with the least foundation, because the other two reminded me of those appalling creatures in department stores with repainted faces and a one-metre exclusion zone of pungent perfume stench around them. On balance, I think my olfactory organ would have just about preferred the urine soaked multi-storey stairwell, given the choice. By sheer coincidence, I had chosen Tina herself, and I have to report that she was a personable and helpful lady of some fifty summers, with a nice, broad Black Country accent. I sat down and explained the purpose of my visit. She was about to launch into her spiel when the doorbell tinkled and a man in a raincoat and hat (looking more than a little like Inspector Clouseau), came in and headed for the far end of the shop. The Pungent Perfumed Pair simultaneously asked, with identical voices, if he needed assistance – which was quite amusing – but he grumpily explained that he was just browsing. He seemed to be the kind of man for whom politeness came as a real effort, and I felt sure he would have preferred to tell them to eff off.

19

Tina gave him the once-over, leant towards me in conspiratorial fashion and whispered in my ear. She explained that he was 'a bit of a weird bloke' who was always in the shop but had never booked a holiday. I suggested that maybe he just came to peek at the photos of holiday catalogue models in their bikinis; something she confessed she had never thought of. We shelved the theories and returned to the matter in hand. I explained to her that I intended to stay for a month in order to see as much of New Zealand as I could, for several reasons. Firstly, it hardly made sense to travel twelve thousand miles, hand over a carving, pose for a photograph and come home again. If I was to be forced to make this epic voyage I might as well make a holiday of it and actually see the place. By all accounts, it was a beautiful country. This also meant that I wouldn't have to worry about the return flight for a while. Tina suggested that the best and cheapest way to achieve my objective was to hire a motor home. I could arrive in Christchurch, pick up the vehicle from the airport and be off exploring right away, or at least, once the horrendous jetlag had worn off. These motor homes had all the creature comforts – shower, chemical toilet, cooker, fridge, kettle, toaster and so on, and when I'd had enough driving for the day I could pull over and I'd be in my very own cosy flat. She also explained that there were hundreds of well-equipped sites all over New Zealand that offered laundry facilities, TV rooms, showers, and dining rooms, but even more importantly, fellow travellers to chat to. This all sounded fine and dandy, but I expressed grave reservations about the flight. I explained that I was a nervous flyer, and that twenty-four hours in the air was possibly the best cure for constipation I could think of. Tina sympathized and suggested a one day stop-over in Singapore or Los Angeles. I asked her which she'd choose out of the two, and she weighed this carefully.

'It depends what you like, really,' she replied, chewing the top of her Tina's Travel ballpoint until it attained the consistency of old bubble gum. 'If you like clean, modern cities with ninety degree heat, friendly taxi drivers who won't rip you off, an interesting Chinese old town and dirt cheap electrical goods, I'd say Singapore, *and* you can visit the world-famous Raffles Hotel and treat yourself to a Singapore Sling, just like Noel Coward and loads of other movie stars used to do. On the other hand, you can stay in L.A. and risk getting shot by a Latino gang.'

I gave this careful consideration, and chose Singapore.

We discussed timings, airports and so on, and I signed on the dotted line for a flight the following week from Manchester, via Singapore, to Christchurch. After studying Tina's map for a while, I decided to explore the South Island first, and then take the car ferry to the North Island to do likewise there. I would fetch up at Rotorua a few days before I was due to fly home from Auckland, hand over Mr Maori, and Bob's your uncle, I'd be a rich man. Only Bob wasn't my uncle; Ken was, so something told me it wouldn't be that simple. My first real problem was the airfare. As I think I mentioned earlier, I'd not had the best of years, financially speaking, and a thousand quid for a flight was beyond my means, as was the hire fee for the motor home, not to mention eating out for a whole month, camp site fees, diesel, and a huge list of not-to-be-missed, once-in-a-lifetime excursions. I'd be stark raving mad, explained Tina, if I didn't swim with the dolphins, go whale-watching, see the penguins returning home after fishing in the ocean all day, visit the glow-worm caves, go white-water rafting, bungee jump off the Sky Tower in Auckland, take the Shotover Canyon Jet Boat in Queenstown, parachute from a plane or climb Mount Cook.

I explained patiently that I would, in fact, be stark raving mad if I actually *did* any of those things, so we politely agreed to differ. I gave her my details, signed away my life, handed her my over-stretched credit card with clenched buttocks and gritted teeth, and, transactions concluded, said thank you and goodbye.

I drove the short distance home wondering what on earth I'd signed up to, cursing myself for being a slave to the Great God Money. With a heavy sigh – my umpteenth of the day – I parked the car, removed my precious cargo and pulled down the battered

21

garage door with the freshly graffitied tag 'Bazza' on it. If I ever manage to catch the little shit who did that the day after I painstakingly repainted the bloody thing, I swear I'll swing for him.

I unlocked the front door and placed the two boxes side by side in my living room. I still hadn't had a chance to see what was in the larger box, so I put the kettle on and knelt down to take a look, my poor thirty-seven-year-old knees cracking like pistol shots. I lifted the flap of the box, and was about to peek inside when I was interrupted by the sound of my front doorbell. Wearily, I rose again and shuffled back to the front door, cursing under my breath. I was very tired and hungry, and not in the mood for an impromptu visit. I wasn't expecting anyone in particular, and the milkman always came on a Friday, so I knew it wasn't him. I opened the door a few inches, in case it was a Jehovah's Witness, or even worse, a double-glazing salesman. It was neither, but if anything, it was potentially worse still.

It was the police.

23

CHAPTER 3

In which I am made an offer that I can't afford to refuse – once I have run it past Len, the Psychic Dog.

I opened the door fully, once I realized who had come a-calling, and my first reaction was to panic, thinking that one of my family had been involved in an accident. The officers quickly put my mind at rest, and asked if they could come in. One of them was of average height and ugly, whereas the other was virtually a giant, and uglier still. They followed me into the living room – the tall one having to bow his head to get through the door frame – and sat themselves down on my settee without asking. This seemed to greatly upset Len, my psychic dog, who began to growl at the tall one, much to my embarrassment. I ushered him into the kitchen (Len, not the copper) and shut the door behind him, something I know he hates, dropping one of his beef-flavoured chews onto the floor to keep him occupied.

Incidentally, I am fully cognizant of the fact that I teasingly referred to Len as my 'psychic' dog, and then offered no explanation whatsoever. I would beg you to be patient for a while, and all will be revealed in the fullness of time. For the moment, I have a tale to unfold, and if I get ahead of myself, I will become befuddled.

I returned to the living room, apologizing profusely for Len's behaviour. He'd had it in for tall people since he was a puppy, I told the officer, and I assured him that it was nothing personal.

The policeman gave me a watery smile that constituted his reply in full, and even that appeared to pain him. The smaller one leaned towards me and opened the dialogue.

'Firstly, sir,' he began, 'you are not in trouble, and you have done absolutely nothing wrong. We must make that clear.'

I breathed a sigh of relief and begged him to continue.

'What we have come to see you about is highly confidential, and must go no further. By this, I mean, not even to your family – not even to your dog. Is that understood?'

I said that it was.

He leaned even further towards me, so that I was able to detect the previous night's tandoori chicken. 'We need a civilian to help us with an operation that will benefit our country, no less, and other countries too. You have been chosen because you fit the profile, and because we know you are about to travel to Singapore. That is correct, isn't it?'

I was astounded. I'd only seen Tina an hour before, and already the police knew my every move. I wondered whether Tina was an undercover MI5 agent, and asked the officer for an explanation.

'I must apologize for what must seem to you like a scene from Orwell's 1984, sir,' he explained, 'but ticket sales to Singapore are being monitored, and names and addresses are being matched with information we hold at HQ. We can instantly tell if the person buying a plane ticket is a certain age, married, divorced, has a criminal record, a drugs conviction or whatever. The majority who are not suitable for our operation are duly discounted, leaving the few drips at the other end of the funnel, so to speak, to choose from. And you're one of those drips, sir. You appear to have led a crime-free life, you're fairly respectable, and you're off to Singapore. Work or pleasure is it?'

'You tell me,' I quipped. 'You seem to know everything about me. What's my inside leg measurement then?'

'Thirty-two,' he snapped back.

Well, he was only spot-on! I presume it was speculation, but it unnerved me nevertheless. My mind was racing as I tried to anticipate the reason for their visit. Their speed was nothing short of uncanny, but I had to wonder at their intelligence, and by that I mean the intelligence at their disposal, not their I.Q. The tall one would have struggled to hit double figures in that regard, whereas the smaller chap seemed to be the sharp one who elected to do all the talking. Presumably, Big Boy was just there to give me a slap if I wouldn't play ball, or maybe I just had an overactive imagination as a result of watching too many American cop dramas. Where was I? Oh yes, I was questioning their intelligence, vis-à-vis my unblemished record. Had they done their homework properly, they'd have unearthed the fact that I had been constantly harassed by their fellow officers quite recently when my late Uncle Jim was murdered by the psychopathic locksmith. I had two equally ugly coppers on my back throughout that fiasco, and, incredibly, they were convinced that I'd done it. Look, it's a long and involved story, and if I regurgitate that now, I'll never get anywhere, so if you are interested, I advise you to invest in a copy of my previous memoir, entitled 'The Curious Tale of the Missing Hoof' – I can't remember the ISBN offhand, but most good bookshops will order it for you. In fact, if you'll just bear with me a second – yes, it's 978-0-9551428-7-1. Anyway, the point I'm trying to make is; these current coppers weren't as thorough as they liked to think they were, or they'd have discovered that I was under constant police observation only the previous year, until I did their dirty work for them and handed them the psycho locksmith on a plate with watercress around him. *And* I'd got points on my licence for doing thirty-five in a thirty zone. Maybe, I reasoned, my file had been wiped when my uncle's killer was arrested, and the speeding offence wasn't serious enough to put them off.

The small one got down to the nitty-gritty, except that he pronounced it *nittoi-grittoi* because he was from Birmingham.

'We would like you to help us test the security at Singapore Airport,' he began, 'if you are willing. There is no risk whatsoever to your well-being, and Undercover Services, or US as we call it, are willing to pay you handsomely if you co-operate.'

Suddenly, I was a tad more interested. 'When you say handsomely, how handsome are we talking?' I asked. 'Pierce Brosnan? David Beckham? Wayne Rooney? You?'

The officer cracked his face at last. 'Very funny. We'd pay for your flight to New Zealand and your hotel in Singapore. How's that?'

'*That* depends on what you want me to do.'

He lifted his black briefcase from the floor and sat it on his lap. 'Okay. We suspect that Singapore Airport's security staff are, shall we say, either useless or dodgy. Intelligence tells us that sizeable quantities of heroin have been smuggled through there and the smugglers have got away with it time and time again, in spite of the sniffer dogs and the random searches. We are working in conjunction with the Singapore government to find out what is going wrong, and we need an undercover guy with a spotless record to test the system for us. We will secrete a large quantity of the drug within your luggage and hide tracker devices inside the packages. Then we intend to alert the security staff that someone on your flight, i.e. you, is suspected of drug trafficking and see what unfolds. We think that somehow the baggage handlers might be getting wind of it and stealing the goods before they arrive at security, or maybe security themselves are in on the act and selling it on, rather than arresting the culprits. Our undercover man in Singapore, who has infiltrated the gangs, tells us that there are stories of drug traffickers that have hidden heroin in their luggage and cleared customs with no problems, only to find that the goods were missing when they got to their hotel rooms and examined their cases. Then their immediate bosses would naturally accuse them of doing the dirty and ventilate them with machine gun bullets by way of making a point. It's a clever scam if you think

28

about it. The drug boss can hardly complain to the airport that they stole his heroin can he? He'd have to own up that he was trying to smuggle the stuff in the first place.'

I nodded dumbly. I was still in a state of shock.

'To be honest,' he continued, 'we don't know what's going on, hence this little sting operation. There are a few scenarios. One: you'll get arrested and questioned, and they'll find your stash and hand it in to the police, as they should. Two: they simply won't find it and you'll walk through the airport and out into the night; or three: ditto, but when you get to your hotel, your heroin will be missing. Either way, you're in the clear. If you're arrested, fine, we step in and free you right away, or rather, our Singapore counterpart does. If you clear customs, he meets you at the hotel instead, relieves you of the goods and say thanks. If, on reaching your destination, the goods have mysteriously vanished, we'll know there's treachery afoot, and we'll be tracking the progress of the packages with interest. What do you say, Mr Eve?'

'No thanks.'

'I noticed that the tread on the back tyre of your old MG is below the legal limit,' said Big Boy, seemingly apropos of nothing.

'Is that right?' I asked him. 'I must get it changed tomorrow.'

'You should,' he growled, 'and be very careful on the A449. There are lots of speed cameras along there, and I'd hate you to lose your licence, especially if you'd had a drink.' He eyed up my half bottle of Shiraz on the coffee table – the one I intended to have with my dinner – if I was ever going to be allowed to start cooking it. I am an astute fellow, and I could see where all this was leading. They were clumsily applying pressure.

'I don't care for threats,' I snapped, 'and especially not your very thinly-veiled ones. It was hardly subtle was it, officer? It hardly shuffled shyly into the room wearing a burqa, avoiding eye contact did it? Talk about heavy-handed. 'If you don't co-operate, we'll do you for every minor offence we can invent, including wearing a loud shirt in a built-up neighbourhood after dusk'. You can't just bludgeon your way into people's houses and demand that they smuggle drugs for you, you know. What happened to human rights?'

The smaller policeman apologized for his friend, explaining that he was passionate about nailing drug smugglers, and sometimes this frustrated him to the point where his methods became a little less subtle than they should have been. I accepted the apology and we all calmed down a bit.

'The trouble is,' the officer continued, 'no one *ever* wants to help us, which is understandable. We all like the quiet life, and that's okay, but drugs are killing thousands of people all over the world. They are pure evil in powder form, and sometimes we feel like Old King Cole, trying in vain to get the waves to recede.'

'King Canute,' I interjected.

'Oh, right – I knew it began with a K. But you see what I mean, don't you? We're all good at condemning these people, but who's willing to help the police to eradicate the scum? No one, that's who!'

I am a conscientious fellow, and he had wounded me in my Achilles Heel. He just looked at me pitifully now, a bit like a Labrador puppy in a cage at a rescue centre, only nowhere near as cute.

'If I did help you,' I asked resignedly, 'you would guarantee that I was not held in some filthy Singapore jail with murderers and rapists who might wish to bugger me or slit my throat or both, even temporarily? By that I mean held temporarily, not have my throat cut temporarily of course. I realize that that's more permanent.'

The small one resumed. 'Absolutely. *If* you were arrested – and at present that's a big 'if' – our people would be on hand to get you off, let's say within an hour, maximum, once your identity had been verified.'

'And why can't you get one of your coppers to do this?' I asked, not unreasonably.

'Good question,' he conceded. 'I could give you eight good reasons why they couldn't, but I wouldn't want to bore you to death. Firstly, we are seriously stretched as a unit. We simply can't afford to send men all that way and have them away for a week, when they're desperately needed back here. Secondly, coppers are easy to spot, and the criminals are onto us right away. Lord knows why. Maybe it's our size twelve feet and the way we walk together in unison, like the title sequence of The Bill.'

He then proceeded to list the other six reasons and bored me to death, even though he'd promised not to. I begged him to cease, and reluctantly agreed to think about it overnight and give him my answer in the morning. I could see he wasn't greatly impressed with this; a bit like those vacuum cleaner salesmen aren't when, after a three hour grilling, you ask for time to reflect. They like the paperwork signed there and then, so that their commission is guaranteed. I half expected him to pretend that he was phoning his boss back at the office to see if he could up the fee, but thankfully, he didn't resort to that particular pile of old baloney.

We agreed that he could ring after breakfast, and I would give him my answer. Whilst I won't say that he was exactly sweetness and light at that point, it eventually seemed to satisfy him. The two men stood up and we shook hands. A muffled growl came from somewhere deep inside the kitchen as if to underline my intention to wrap the discussion up and get shut of them, sharpish. I had a dinner to cook, and Len would want a walk round the block before we settled for the night.

I saw them out and walked into the kitchen to retrieve Len and throw together my humble meal. As I tried in vain to defrost something resembling the flesh of a mummified dinosaur that had met its death in a glacier during the cretaceous period, I couldn't help wondering what on earth I was getting into. I was just about the most law-abiding person I knew, a fervent anti-drugs campaigner and, to cap it all, a person who hated travelling long distances in the air. Now, all of a sudden, I was signing up for a fourteen hour plane trip to the Far East, in order to smuggle heroin. I moodily forked in the dinosaur steak and frozen mixed veg, which was so grim that even Len didn't beg for some of it. What I really needed at that juncture was a spot of fresh air to help me think. In addition to this, and just for fun you understand, I wanted to see what Len thought.

Now, to put the record straight, before you accuse me of being a crackpot, I don't *really* think my dog is psychic. It's just that one day, when he did his business and I was about to scoop it up like a responsible pet owner should, I noticed the configuration of his output was interesting. There were three pieces in total, quite short and stumpy, and arranged like the letter Y, if you follow me. I thought no more about it till the following day, when he produced three of them again, but this time configured like the letter N. Well, this intrigued me. In my mind they were saying YES and NO. From then on, I closely observed Len's waste products and began to make a chart of the many arrangements that he came up with. And why not, I say. For centuries, people have read tea leaves, gazed into crystal balls and studied tarot cards, so why not Mystic Len's poo?

I know we're going off the point a bit here, but each day I would, in a tongue-in-cheek fashion, seek Len's advice on the burning question of the moment, and see what he came up with. For example, I would ask, 'Mystic Len, should I buy a lottery ticket this week?' and Len would do his stuff. If the Y came up, I'd invest, and if it was the N, I wouldn't. Remarkably, his success rate was incredibly high, even though, unlike my uncle, I only usually won a tenner. Of course, he had a much more varied repertoire that just Y and N, so I felt it necessary to compile a list of symbols and attribute to each one a clear meaning. I have listed a random sample of the more common ones, with my interpretations.

Y

Yes

N

No

T

Think carefully: don't be hasty

Stonehenge

(When several actually stand upright) A sacrifice is called for

Chopsticks

Eat out at the Cantonese buffet instead of cooking tonight

Broken Breadstick

Eat out at Luciano's instead of cooking tonight

Exclamation Mark

Danger!

Five Barred Gate

A mental or physical barrier in my way

Cricket Stumps

A good omen, unless they are in disarray

Melted Chocolate

(Not my favourite) Messy situation needs addressing

Well, I could go on, but I have at least thirty more and it could get tedious, not to mention distasteful. I put Len's lead on and we trotted around the block until we got to the point where he usually gets creative. I could see he was brewing up, so I pulled out my plastic Spar bag and a few sheets of kitchen roll and tried my best not to make eye contact with the old bag twitching the curtains across the road.

Len grunted a bit – I think he was slightly constipated due to guzzling my giant-sized bag of peanuts without permission the previous day – and crouched down ready to do his thing. I quickly asked him the question that was vexing me, which was, 'Len, should I help the police?' and immediately my trusty dog issued forth with what was a full and frank answer. He backed off in order that I could view his nut-encrusted handiwork, and began to scratch away at the dusty paving slabs with his back legs in order to cover up the mess, missing the foul stuff by a country mile, like all dogs do.

I flicked on my torch, as it was now quite dark, knelt down to study the evil waste product, and what I saw made the hairs on the back of my neck stand up, not to mention making the hairs up my nose shrivel.

Len's message was crystal clear. It said: 'Y!' (Len didn't do the inverted commas, by the way. I added those.)

I knew right away that this meant I should go to Singapore and help the police, but I would potentially be putting myself in danger. At this juncture I half expected to hear those three dramatic power chords they always use in suspense thrillers, but nothing happened. All I could hear was the wind rustling the trees in Bridle Road and a shrill, distant voice shouting, 'I hope you're going to pick that up!'

I duly gathered up Mystic Len's pungent prediction and dropped it into the Spar bag, sealing the opening with a tight knot. I waved a sarcastic wave in the direction of Mrs Curtain Twitcher and dragged my gifted pet down the road towards home. It was a cold, misty February evening and I was not dressed for it. I still had a glass of Shiraz left in the bottle, and I desperately needed it to be in me. Adam Eve, upstanding citizen, was about to do his duty. I was going to smuggle half a dozen bags of heroin into Singapore.

CHAPTER 4

In which I take delivery of my vile cargo and set off on the first leg of my journey.

First thing Wednesday morning the average-sized copper arrived at my door and asked to be allowed inside. I remarked that he hadn't bought Herman Munster's uglier brother with him this time, and he allowed himself a dry half-smile. He was in plain clothes and I commented on this, by way of making small talk. He explained that he was about to meet a man at the motorway services in Worcester in order to buy ten thousand pounds worth of cocaine from him. I asked if it was for the station's staff party, and he gave me the other half of his earlier smile. The fellow smiled as if he'd been allocated just fifty to last him a lifetime, and he was scared of using them up too soon. We sat on the settee again, just like we had the previous night, with Len locked away in the kitchen nibbling on his chew-stick. The policeman lifted the black briefcase onto his lap, just as he had done before, but this time he opened it. Inside were rows of plastic bags full of white powder. I suddenly felt as if I were in an episode of Miami Vice. I'd witnessed this scene so many times before, usually in squalid Latino apartments, and to be a part of it myself just felt downright weird. I was tempted to ask if I could dip my finger into an open bag and taste the merchandise, but as I had no idea what heroin was supposed to taste like anyway, I didn't bother.

'There are six kilos of very pure stuff here,' he began, 'and it's worth a lot of money. We've used the real thing so that the sniffer dogs can detect it, if they're around. Each bag contains a minute tracker device, so we know where it is and who's got it. I'm relying on you to keep absolutely schtum about this, and hide it away securely until your flight. When you're packing, wrap it like a present for Aunt Jemima, maybe, and put it under your clothing in your main suitcase. Don't carry it in your hand luggage, and remember: this stuff was confiscated during a big raid in Wolverhampton a few years ago. We know how much there is, to the gram. We'd take a dim view if you sold some to any of your friends, understood?'

I gave him a scornful look. What kind of people did he think I hung around with, for goodness sake? Most of my friends and family wouldn't have known what to do with the evil stuff if they were given it. I had some vague idea that you sort of sniffed it, but I might have been getting confused with cocaine. It's a shame my uncle wasn't still alive. He'd have known, for sure.

I excused myself and hid the bags away in my bedroom in case Len found one and decided to tear them to bits. What I certainly didn't need in my increasingly complicated life was a drug-addict dog. Just imagine coming home to find him shooting up in the kitchen, if that's the correct expression, or going out by himself at night so that he could hold up the Indian corner shop in order fund his next fix.

I returned to the living room to find the police officer helping himself to my last chocolate digestive. I stiffened the lip and said nothing, though my anguish would have been palpable to a more sensitive man. A thought had occurred to me while I was upstairs, and I needed an answer. Did the people at Manchester airport know anything about this operation? I'd forgotten that I first had to clear *their* customs, before I could even think about Singapore's. He explained that they *were* in the know, and I'd be allowed to sail through, unhindered. This put my mind at rest more than somewhat. I saw him out and he wished me 'bon voyage', promising to be in touch if need be. I was just about to broach the subject of payment in my usual, embarrassed way, when he reached into the inside pocket of his suit and produced an envelope with 'Mr Eve' written on it, with a little twiddly flourish underneath.

'One thousand, five hundred pounds,' he said, glancing around him furtively as he did so. 'And can I thank you on behalf of Undercover Services. If there were more people like you, we'd be a damned sight better off. Oh, and I thought you'd appreciate cash, and not a bouncing cheque signed by Mr Barnes-Wallace.'

I thanked him sincerely – I was stony broke. 'How do I get in touch, if I'm desperate?' I asked, as he headed down the drive to his car.

'You don't,' he called. 'We get in touch with you. You'll be watched every step of the way.' And with that, he was gone.

I walked back into the flat feeling as if I was in a Hollywood thriller; the sort that Tom Cruise or Matt Damon are always in, where they have to work undercover and risk getting found out by the burly, tattooed Hispanic drug runners with AK47s and nasty growly dogs. Part of me felt petrified, I have to admit, but there was another part of me that was really coming alive for the first time. I felt a frisson of pure undiluted excitement shudder through my frame that I'd never experienced before, and I couldn't wait until Friday. I tore open the envelope impatiently, and inside, as promised, was an impressive wad of bank notes. I toyed with the idea of throwing them into the air and shouting, 'I'm rich – rich do you hear me? Rich beyond my wildest dreams!' as they cascaded down, but Len was observing closely, and he had been known to devour the occasional misplaced banknote in the past, so I reluctantly decided against it. Even in a state of euphoria, I was Captain Sensible.

Once this euphoria had subsided a little, I pressed on with the practical arrangements for my trip. I informed my family of course, omitting the small insignificant detail about me being an international drug courier. My parents offered to look after Len, just as I was plucking up the courage to air the subject, so that was

39

handy. I'd never been away from him for more than two days before, and I was dreading that part. I kept wondering if he'd recognize me when I returned, and even worse, if he decided that he liked it better at their house, preferred my mother's cooking and didn't want to come home again. I rang my brother Steven, who, by way of background information, is a well known and successful comedy playwright, and said that I'd ring regularly while I was away, and of course I rang my ex-wife, Katie and my children, Jack and Lauren, promising lots of presents upon my return. It was especially hard being without either of them for a whole month, so I intended to spoil them, courtesy of my forthcoming windfall.

Then I rang Dozy Derek, my tame taxi driver. Derek was to scintillating conversation what Hitler was to ballroom dancing, but my motto was 'better the devil you know'. I had used him for years, and he was comfortable, like an old shoe. True, he could make a conversation about the weather last from here till London, and he could have done with an underarm deodorant, but at least he didn't scare the living shit out of me with his erratic driving or subject me to constant, loud crackly messages in Punjabi from his controller. Dozy Derek was a one-man business, and I liked that. He didn't need an intercom. If he got too boring for words, I simply pretended I was tired and nodded off.

Luckily, Derek was free to take me to Manchester and also bring me back, which saved me from leaving my old car at the airport for four weeks. The bad news was, he was picking me up at six in the morning, which meant I'd have to be up at five. Obviously, I'd heard of five o'clock a.m., but I'd never actually experienced it, and the thought of that filled me with a nameless fear. That evening, I borrowed several books about New Zealand from the library and, after a plate of fish fingers, peas and oven chips, washed down with a half bottle of Chianti (I know how to live), I gave them my full attention.

The first thing I learnt was that New Zealand was approximately the same size as Britain, but obviously separated into two islands.

40

Its population is around four million, as opposed to our *sixty* four million (or has it gone up again?), and incredibly, a third of those people live in and around Auckland. I tried to imagine this, and conjured up an image of a completely deserted country, like in one of those disaster movies where the inhabitants have been wiped out by a virus.

I also learnt that the Kiwi accent was quite different to the Australian one. I must confess that I thought both countries were virtually indistinguishable and only a few miles apart, but again, I was wrong. The nearest bit of New Zealand is a staggering seven hundred or so miles past Australia, and the accent is, curiously, a hybrid of Aussie and a mild South African, with the letters 'A' and 'E' pronounced as an 'I', and, perversely, the letter 'I' often pronounced as an 'A'. In fact, the New Zealanders seemed to love mangling their vowels just for the hell of it, if I was to believe my library book. It cited the example of 'Fish and Chips', which becomes 'Fash and Chaps', and also the word 'Accent' itself, which becomes 'Iccint'.

I happen to know that this is true, because of my friend Malcolm. Malcolm is a radio presenter at the BBC, and one day he was given the task of interviewing an eminent New Zealand scientist at the Think-Tank Centre in Birmingham, as he peered down his powerful microscope.

'What are you studying?' asked Malcolm, whereupon the New Zealand chap replied, 'Cells from lipids.'

Malcolm had heard of lipids, and vaguely knew they were something to do with body fats, but he wasn't really sure, so he asked the scientist to explain what they were, just to be on the safe side. The scientist looked at him askance, and replied, 'Surely everyone knows what lipids are?'

Malcolm, feeling very ill-educated all of a sudden, begged to differ. He offered the opinion that he was surely not alone in his ignorance, and suggested that the average man in the street would not know what a lipid was. The impatient scientist, frustrated beyond belief now, and looking a little flushed, explained:

'Good God, man, surely you know what a lipid is. Large wild cat, covered in spots? Fastest creature on four legs? What do they teach you in English schools?'

Now, you might think that this is just me regurgitating some hackneyed old joke, but it isn't. I actually heard this exchange on the radio with my own ears as I was driving to a client's offices, and I nearly swerved off the road, I was laughing so much.

Anyway, I've digressed again – something that I often do without realizing it, and I apologize. I was telling you, before I got side-tracked with body fats and leopards, that I was being very diligent, as all good writers should be, and doing my research. I found out that North Island was more tropical in places, with areas of rainforest, waterfalls and palm trees, and far more Maori influence in terms of town names, but also with very English countryside, whereas South Island was more dramatic, with snow-capped mountain ranges, fiords, wild rivers and so on – a bit like Wales but with nice people. It was here that I had planned to explore first, so that I could fetch up in Rotorua near the end of my stay for the big finale at the Maori Museum. Even at this early stage, I was beginning to question the wisdom of this decision, made in haste at the office of Tina's Travel. Perhaps, with hindsight, it might have been better to get the presentation of Mr Maori over with so that I could unwind afterwards. It also meant that I was going to have to look after the foul old carving for almost the entire duration of my visit, rather than simply off-loading it in the first week, and that was just bound to cause stress, as if I hadn't got enough on my plate with my new drug-smuggling business and all. I cursed my hasty decision-making – often the bane of my life, but there was nothing I could do. I was stuck with Plan A now, as I had booked the flights, so that, as they say, was that. I had made my camper van fold-down bed and I was going to have to lie in it, with Mr Maori by my side for company, probably.

That evening I had another one of my weird dreams. This time, predictably I suppose, I was tied up by bad men and left in a desert, and a leopard (or lipid) was gnawing off my toes one at a time. I woke up screaming, and seconds later, I was feeling very foolish indeed. I couldn't settle after that, not that I needed to as it was after nine anyway, so I decided to pack my things well in advance for a change. I dragged my old blue suitcase from under the bed and began to sling stuff into it. My in-depth research revealed that it would be pleasantly hot, like an English summer (ha ha!), with temperatures beginning to dip at night, now that autumn was approaching. This caused me great concern, having to cater for hot days and cold evenings, and before long it dawned on me that I'd simply thrown every single item of clothing I possessed at my suitcase. It became patently obvious early on that there was no way it would accommodate even a quarter of it, let alone the six kilos of heroin, a.k.a. my gift-wrapped present for fictional Aunt Jemima. However, I tried to imagine how many pairs of boxers I'd need for a whole month, and then how many coats, shirts, socks, trousers, shorts and so on, and suddenly my initial estimate didn't look so far out. In fact, I'd probably underdone it, but unless I purchased at least another ten suitcases from the local pound shop and hired a team of Sherpas, it wasn't going to happen. I paced the room and tried to think minimal. Did I really need two dinner suits? Or a choice of sixteen jumpers for the cold evenings? Was I ever going to get a chance to model that Edwardian smoking jacket on a 'Top Ten' campsite?

Okay, so I'm being a bit flippant, but I had initially thrown in my best suit, just because I always did when staying places in England. I'd heard that New Zealand was very casual, dress-wise, so the suit became the first casualty, so to speak. I had to remind myself that when one was in Romania, one did what the Romans did. I also remembered that the camp sites all had laundry facilities, so I didn't need thirty pairs of boxer shorts either. Seven would do, and when they were past their sell-by, I'd have to wash them. This new, minimalist zeal was starting to kick in now, and I began to cull my shirts next. I quickly went from thirty shirts to three, and then hacked away at the jumper population until I was left with one tatty old fleece. The trousers diminished from ten pairs to two, and I threw in a rather ancient pair of khaki shorts to keep them company. A few cosmetics, a spare pair of trainers, the RayBans I won by answering a simple question and sending off ten coupons from my toothpaste boxes, and my trusty England cricket cap completed the ensemble, plus of course my passport and driver's licence. I wrapped the evil powder as suggested, in a crumpled and disgustingly cheerful Christmassy sheet of paper that I found in a cupboard, and even sellotaped a gift tag to it to finish it off. Lord knows what customs would think if they did stumble across it, it being almost March.

I also dug out my smelly backpack to go as hand luggage – the one I bought for six quid from Fort William when I climbed Ben Nevis in 2006. I'd left a banana in it for about a year, and when I looked inside, it was as if an incontinent rodent had slowly decomposed in there. I must have spent an hour fumigating the thing, and even to this day it has a strange aroma. This unsavoury receptacle was going to have to be Mr Maori's home for the duration of the two flights. I cocooned him in two layers of bubble wrap and packed him away carefully. After all, he was my meal ticket, unattractive as he was.

Once everything was stowed and positioned by the front door ready for the early start, I became very restless. I paced the floor like a caged tiger and by mid-afternoon I had graduated to a bored polar bear, like the one that used to be at Dudley Zoo. It would just swing its head from side to side, like a mental patient in an asylum, and it was quite upsetting to witness. I decided to load Len into the MG and deliver him to my parents' house, just to break up the day. I stayed an hour, drank a gallon of tea and slipped away as silently as I could so that he wouldn't bark after me. I don't mind admitting that I shed an unmanly tear on the way back. I imagined, in a rather maudlin fashion, that something tragic might befall me, causing me to die a lonely death twelve thousand miles from home, and my poor, bewildered little dog would mourn forever, never understanding why his master had not returned. Jeez, this was getting heavy! I popped my *Best of Split Enz* CD into the player just to try to get myself into an antipodean mood and take my mind off Len.

That evening, bored with the TV but too excited to go to bed, I began my pacing tiger routine again, and as I was in mid-pace betwixt armchair and kitchen, I noticed the old box that Mr Chance had given me, containing my Uncle Ken's bric-a-brac. This, I felt sure, would entertain me for the final half-hour before I turned in, so I hauled it up onto the settee and ripped open the parcel tape that was securing the flaps. I can't say I was expecting much, and in that regard I was not disappointed. There were a few old books, an old Napoleon's hat-shaped mantelpiece clock, a Swiss army knife with an attachment for removing horses' hoofs and another for street stabbings, a metal Spitfire aeroplane on a plinth, an unopened joke shop false beard in a plastic bag, a German army helmet, a school tie, an old photo of a very attractive, dark-skinned woman in a battered brass frame and, bizarrely, a pair of real handcuffs with a little key sellotaped to them. Lord knows what he used these for, and I shuddered to think. Maybe he liked to spice up his love life with the dark-skinned woman, whoever she was. I could only speculate. Finally, there was a bundle of old, musty smelling letters tied together with a piece of string. Now, I don't know about you, but I always find stuff like that fascinating; you know, delving into old, private correspondence. I decided to pour myself a soothing brandy and dry ginger, just to help me nod off, and while I was sipping at it, peek at the letters. Then, for some inexplicable reason, I deviated from this plan to fiddle with the handcuffs. Maybe the spirit of Houdini in me thought he would enjoy the challenge of trying to escape from them – I don't know. I'd never tried on a real pair before, and I suppose the lure of them was just too great to resist. Besides, I had the key so there was no great danger involved. I laid the letters down beside me and placed the one cuff on my right hand, clicking it shut. I decided against putting the other one on, just in case. I was cavalier and devil-may-care, but only up to a point. Then I tried to wriggle free, but it was impossible. These were the real McCoy – solid metal heavyweight cuffs; probably police or military equipment – not your everyday pink fluffy plastic ones for bedroom use.

I gave up trying to be the great escapologist, deciding that it wasn't really a good career move, and removed the tape that held the key to the other cuff. I pushed it into the lock, and was immediately unimpressed by its design. Instead of the satisfying clunk I had hoped for, it just wiggled around aimlessly inside, like it was three sizes too small. This puzzled me no-end, until I had a sudden brainwave. I tried it in the mantel clock, and you'll never guess what. It fitted beautifully. The clock began to tick away like a good 'un, which meant that, at worst, I'd at least be able to accurately record how long I'd been trapped in the handcuffs, should I so choose.

I was sweating now, because in less than ten hours' time, I was to begin my epic voyage down under. Leg irons, shackles and other restraining devices may well have been *de rigueur* for travelling there in Victorian times, but they looked out of place on the modern commuter. I grabbed the torch and went out to the tool shed in search of my hacksaw, only to suddenly remember that I had lent it to my brother the week before, as a prop for one of his plays. Then, the awful realization swept over me like a wave of nausea, that this saw was my first and last hope, short of melting the thing off in the fire, and my hand with it.

Unless a miracle happened, and quickly at that, I was going to have to travel to the other end of the earth and bluff my way through four sets of customs officers (not to mention enduring the incredulous stares of my fellow passengers) sporting a dangling handcuff. Life didn't get much better than that. I swigged off the remaining brandy, by way of easing my mental anguish, and staggered off to bed, eager to see what the theme of the night's dream would be. If only Len had been with me, then maybe his teatime 'number two' could have forewarned me, but in fairness, even a dog of his undoubted talents would have struggled to create a handcuffs motif out of shit.

CHAPTER 5

*In which Derek and I both get the wrong end of the stick, and I
have some explaining to do.*

Isn't it deeply frustrating when you're shattered, but still can't
sleep? My brain insisted on spewing out garbage as I lay there
tossing and turning, and I could not turn it off. It was like a
computer that had gone horribly wrong, thanks to some virus or
other, and was processing pure gobbledegook. I told myself to
relax, but all I was really doing was repeating the word 'relax' like
a mantra, and not relaxing at all. Then I began to sing a song in my
head – 'I Hope I Never Have to See You Again' it was, by New
Zealand's own *Split Enz*, and after twenty consecutive full
renditions of it I was flagging. It was as if my mind had split into
two warring factions, or enz, I suppose you could say, each intent
on destroying the other. Not that I hate the song; far from it, but I
just didn't want it to become a tape-loop in my skull for the rest of
time. After an hour of this, I begged it to stop; literally begged it,
and when it wouldn't, I tried to fill my head with something else
to displace it. This did actually work, but then I became fixated on
the new distraction instead, which was, if I recall, the 'To be or
not to be' soliloquy from Hamlet. Deranged by now, I asked
myself for total silence, and for about five seconds I succeeded,
but then my inner demons began battling it out again, and before
long I was singing that damned song again.

This was the last straw. I had to get up and visit the bathroom,
and thankfully the delirium seemed to subside once I had risen. I

49

sat, bleary-eyed on the toilet seat, examining my handcuffed right hand and wondering what on earth I could do to disguise it on the plane. I tried on my dressing gown and pulled the unattached handcuff back up my arm. If I secured it with masking tape, I could just about get away with it, but the result didn't do me any favours. It looked as if someone, a wrestler maybe, had tied my forearm into several ugly knots. I could have suffered the aesthetic aspect, however, had the physical side been okay, but it wasn't. The handcuff was already rubbing my wrist badly, and when I tried to hide the other bit up my sleeve it seemed to cut off my circulation.

I crawled back into bed with that resigned attitude that people like me, who seem to court chaos on a regular basis, assume in order to stop us from slashing our wrists in a frenzy of self-loathing. I lay down on my side with my cuffed hand upper-most, but the spare handcuff swung down and clattered into my testicles, causing me to briefly become nauseous and cross-eyed with the pain. I turned over, but then I found I was lying on the things (my handcuffs I mean, not my testicles), which was completely unworkable. Eventually, after a few heartfelt expletives, I lay on my back and eventually dropped off into a deep sleep from which I was rudely awoken what seemed like ten minutes later by my alarm clock. I swung my arm over quickly to turn it off, and in so doing, also swung the loose handcuff, which smacked me forcibly in the face, gashing my eyebrow. To literally add insult to injury, I then discovered that it was not five o'clock as I had imagined, but a quarter to four, and I'd apparently set the alarm incorrectly. Now I was awake once more, with a throbbing, bleeding eyebrow. Too tired to even dab it, I reset the alarm with trembling hand, pushed my face into the pillow and somehow managed to drop off.

An hour later, I was awake once more, but this time my body clock had done its work before the alarm had the chance to, which was just as well, as I later discovered that I'd accidentally set it for half-past ten. My face was still pushed into the pillow, where I'd left it an hour before, so I pushed myself up, and curiously the pillow came with me. It was then that I realized the extent of my gash. My pillow and I were stuck together with dried blood; about half a pint of it at a guess. I staggered towards the bathroom, supporting the thing so that it didn't tear my face off, and spent ten minutes or so soaking it with warm water to encourage it to let go of my eyebrow, whining like a mistreated greyhound as I did so.

Eventually we parted company, and I threw it in the washing basket. I swear Sweeney Todd's shaving towels would have looked less gory. I examined my eye in the bathroom mirror and came to the conclusion that I would not pursue my dream of becoming a World Champion heavyweight boxer after all; not if this was how they felt every morning.

To my absolute delight – and I'm being sarcastic here, for those who are slow to latch on to that kind of thing – my handcuffs were not part of one of my weird dreams, but all too real. I crawled into the shower and cleaned myself up, before taping the spare cuff onto my arm. I then threw on my clothes, shaved as best I could with a manacle on and a bunch of clanking muscles I never knew I had, and then clumped downstairs to get on the outside of a few stale cornflakes before Dozy Derek arrived.

Dozy, dependable Derek was, as always, bang on time. We loaded up his new people carrier, double checked the essentials; money, credit card, passport, razor, adaptor, clothes, shoes, drugs (well, I didn't say this out loud), Mr Maori, light reading matter, Uncle Ken's bundle of letters (to read when bored), camera, plane tickets (slight sweat, followed by realization that they were electronic), England cricket cap (just to rub it in with the natives when we trounced New Zealand in the current tests), information about motor home pick up, RayBans and sun cream. All present and correct.

I jumped into the passenger seat, clunked and clicked (my handcuffs were playing up) and then fastened my seatbelt. Derek slipped the vehicle into gear and we glided away in the dark, past the ferocious feral felines, busy biting holes in battalions of black

51

bin bags to plunder Thursday's tuna tins (my English teacher at grammar school often told me I was alliterate), past insomniac milkmen delivering their wares in clinking crates, so that the more sensible people of Stourbridge – those who weren't travelling twelve thousand miles on some damn fool errand – could enjoy their Weetabix three hours later, when the sun came up.

After an in-depth conversation about the pros and cons of the new ring road layout – and by in-depth, I mean possibly more detailed and involved than the council meeting had been when the scheme was finally approved – I made my excuses, settled back into the rather comfortable, reclining seat and dozed off. It was just past the services near Holmes Chapel when I eventually resurfaced, and I'm sure Derek had continued to chat to me for the duration of my nap, completely unconcerned that I wasn't replying to anything he said. I say this, because as I groggily came round from under the ether I could hear him prattling on about some local newspaper article he'd been perusing the night before.

'I read that your Uncle Ken decided to donate his organs,' he said.

This surprised me. Not so much that Ken had given his consent, but more so because I couldn't imagine any hospital wanting them. His liver would have been shot for starters, his eyes were like piss-holes in the snow, his heart had been dodgy for years and his lungs must have been like two discarded crisp packets after all those years of Woodbine abuse.

'Can't see them being much use,' I croaked, my eyes still shut. 'Who would want them, knowing where they'd been?'

'Well, you say that, but beggars can't be choosers,' replied Derek. 'My mother wouldn't say no, if you've got any say in it.'

'Why would I have any say in it?' I asked. 'They hardly involve nephews in these matters you know.'

'I don't know,' continued Derek. 'A word from you might swing it for her, if you don't mind of course.'

52

I sat up in my seat and stared at the dozy bugger with what is usually referred to as an incredulous expression. Had I missed a relevant section of conversation during my catnap, I wondered, or had Derek's brain finally dissolved, thanks to too many airport trips undertaken at unsociable hours?

'So what does your mother want or need then?' I asked, for, with Derek, it was far easier to just go along with the flow sometimes, rather than explain how the world works.

'Well, she plays the piano at the old folk's home on a Wednesday,' he explained, 'but she's really struggling nowadays due to her arthritis, and the keys are very stiff, which doesn't help.'

'I can stop you there, I think,' I interjected. 'There's no medical procedure for that, currently. My grandmother suffers from it. Her hands are all sort of sideways at the ends nowadays. She can't peel potatoes anymore, she tells me.'

Now it was Derek's turn to employ the incredulous look.

'I know they can't do anything,' he said, turning onto the M56 motorway just outside Manchester, 'but if you had a word, she'd still be grateful, as long as they haven't already been promised to someone else of course.'

Well, I don't know about you, but I couldn't make head nor tail of this. I put it down to tiredness, as I'd never had to hold a conversation with anyone at that ungodly hour before. I tried one last time to wring a tiny drop of sense from our conversation before I finally let it go and tried to doze off again.

'What, precisely, does your mother need then?' I asked, as patiently as I could manage.

'Well, it's a bit cheeky really,' admitted Derek. 'She'd be grateful for whichever, but she'd prefer the Yamaha I think.'

'What Yamaha?'

'The Yamaha organ. The paper said he had a Yamaha and a Farfisa that he'd left behind at his ex-wife's place, and he'd donated them to a good home in his will because she wanted shot of them, so if they haven't sorted it yet, I wondered if she could have one for the old folks, because they like to sing 'Roll Out The Barrel' of a Wednesday.'

I don't know if you're the same, but occasionally I completely lose the will to live. I scribbled down my aunt's number and suggested he contact her himself, as I was about to jump on a plane. This seemed to satisfy him, and he spent the final quarter of an hour talking about the extreme air turbulence he'd experienced coming back from Portugal once, for which I thanked him profusely.

We parked up at the drop-off zone. Derek helped me out with my luggage and found me a trolley while I walked around aimlessly in circles like a headless chicken. My stomach was turning cartwheels now, and I just wanted to go home with the boring old git and crawl into bed. By this, I mean my own home, not Derek's of course. I can't think of anything more revolting than slipping into bed with a male taxi driver, except, of course, slipping into bed with two of them. Mind you, an intimate evening with Brian Sewell, the eminent art critic, comes close.

Derek said goodbye, wished me *bon voyage* and sidled off, and I sweated and grunted my way into the departure lounge with a trolley that had a mind of its own. It seemed stubbornly intent on visiting some distant cousin in the nearby Asda instead of going where I wanted it to go. I eventually pitched up at the check-in, more by luck than judgement it has to be said, and joined the snaking queue that spanned at least three postal districts. A fit-looking, perma-tanned young man with highlighted hair and a clipboard positioned himself adjacent to me and gave me the once-over, adding a surreptitious wink for good measure. I winked back, immediately realizing that I had been acknowledged by the powers that be. I would have waved, but I was under-cover, and didn't wish to appear too forward. For some reason, this seemed to unman the fellow, who blushed bright red before sashaying off in the direction of the check-in desk. I must admit that I was already beginning to question the quality of the undercover boys, if this one was anything to go by. He seemed wet behind the ears to me, and, if anything, a bit effeminate.

The queue didn't exactly move with the speed of a startled gazelle, and it was a good hour before I fetched up at the front. The lady behind the counter checked in my luggage and asked if I'd packed the bag myself. I briefly thought of answering that a gentleman didn't do that kind of thing, and that my valet, Dobbs, had packed it for me, but I thought better of it and came clean. I loaded it onto the conveyor belt, collected my passport and walked away, my heart doing paradiddles in my chest as I did so. I decided to get the nasty bit over with, and strode purposefully to the entrance to the gates, where the burly-looking security men were X-raying the hand luggage. A character with all the grace and charm of Sir Alan Sugar suffering a migraine headache asked me to remove virtually ever item of clothing I was wearing and throw it in a plastic tray before walking through the metal detector, and right away I realized that I was in for a rough ride. Like a complete buffoon, I had completely forgotten that my handcuffs would raise the alarm, and I was about to fall at the first hurdle. I couldn't just walk off in the opposite direction now, or they would smell a rat. That said, I could hardly waltz nonchalantly through the metal detector either. I stalled, hummed and hawed a bit, and then thought it best to have a quiet word with Sir Alan, who was not the most receptive fellow I'd ever met, possibly due to the fact that at least sixteen other travellers were already queuing up behind me, tutting tetchily. I took him to one side and asked if he could be discreet, and surprisingly, he agreed.

I must say that in moments of absolute desperation, I can sometimes have flashes of inspiration, and this was such a moment. I explained to him, in a conspiratorial whisper, that my girlfriend and I had said farewell to each other a few hours previously, in a loving and intimate way, before I had set off on my month-long holiday to New Zealand. Cynthia, I told him (I made the name up on the spot so it was the best I could do under pressure), was a passionate and rather liberated young thing who liked to play games, and had handcuffed me behind my back in a playful attempt to prevent me from leaving her, before having her evil way with me. Unfortunately, after releasing my one hand, she dropped the key and neither of us could find the thing by the time my taxi arrived, meaning that I had to depart for down under still wearing my love-cuffs. I added earnestly that it was a good job she hadn't cuffed me to the bedstead, the way she did the week before, or I'll still be there now.

Sir Alan nodded sympathetically, and even raised a half-smile, before summoning two even burlier gentlemen and asking them to roughly manhandle me into a private room, where they invited me to sit on a hard plastic chair and wait for their superior to arrive. Actually, they didn't say that he was their superior in as many words, but he'd have been going some to have been inferior to either of them in my humble opinion. Boy, they were officious.

A door swung open and in marched a small, bespectacled, bald-headed gentleman who wouldn't have looked out of place in a Gestapo uniform. He smiled a thin smile and asked me my name. I told him, as I didn't want Mungo and Jerry to beat it out of me. He then asked me politely to remove my coat and roll up my sleeves, which I sheepishly did.

'It's not what it looks like…' I stammered, but he put a finger to his thin lips and said, 'Shush!' This immediately endeared me to him, I have to say. I whiled away the time by imagining that I was purchasing a shovel from B&Q, for the express purpose of stoving his skull in. So realistic was this daydream, that I even asked the till girl if I could bring it back if I cleaned it thoroughly and kept the receipt.

'Have you ever been a prisoner in one of Her Majesty's jails, or placed under arrest, Mr Eve?' he asked quietly.

'No,' I assured him. 'I'm possibly the most law-abiding person you'll ever meet.'

'And you are asking me to believe that this was a last-minute sex session that went wrong?'

'Er, yes, it was exactly that. I'm not into that kind of thing myself, normally speaking, but...'

'Of course not, sir.'

'But Cynthia is, well, you know...'

'I do. Where did you get the cuffs from? They are hardly the usual sex shop variety are they?'

'I wouldn't know, to be honest,' I replied. 'My uncle left them to me in his will, and I showed them to her, and she, well, you know, got a bit excited by them, sort of thing.'

'Was your uncle a policeman?'

'No, why?'

'These are police-issue cuffs.'

'Ah.'

'So where did he get them from, do you think?'

'There you take me into deep waters,' I replied, smiling sweetly at him. 'He was a bit of a character though, so anything is possible.'

Baldy's piercing blue eyes narrowed, and he studied me the way a cat studies a terrified mouse.

'We're just doing some checks on you,' he eventually informed me. 'We have your passport, so we want to make sure you are who you say you are. We will check the prisons, police stations and the courts, and we'll check that your uncle in, in fact, deceased. We'll check to see if you have a girlfriend called Cynthia too, so if there's anything you want to tell us, now's the time to do so.'

'It's not Cynthia,' I admitted.

'Right.'

'I made that name up because I didn't want her embarrassed.'

'Want *who* embarrassed?'

'The girl who isn't really Cynthia. I called her Cynthia after Cynthia Payne. It seemed like a good alias at the time, for some reason. Cynthia Payne is the lady who-'

'Yes, we know who Cynthia Payne is, thank you,' he replied dryly. 'Would you like a cup of tea? This will take a bit of time.'

'How long?' I asked, panicking. 'I'm supposed to be going to New Zealand on holiday.'

Baldy explained that he would be as quick as possible, but thorough security checks took a little time. I toyed with the idea of explaining who I really was, and about my covert drug-smuggling activities, but something told me that this would do nothing to speed up the proceedings. I was also unsure about who was in on the operation and who wasn't, so I buttoned it and stared at the wall. After what seemed like five minutes of awkward silence, but was probably only four, the perma-tanned man with the highlighted hair walked in with a tea tray, smiled at me in a knowing way and placed a plastic cup on the table. My instincts told me that this time around my tea wouldn't still be too hot by the time my interview was concluded. He whispered something or other to Baldy and sat down on a settee, perusing an official-looking document.

Baldy broke the silence.

'What's your girlfriend's name then?'

'I'd rather not say, if you don't mind.'

'Is that because you haven't got one, Adam?'

'Er, no,' I replied, shocked that he'd been able to ascertain this information so quickly, 'What do you mean?'

'Can we be frank? I think that you are a gay gentleman who is trying to protect a male lover. Maybe close friends don't know that you are gay. Perhaps your friend isn't out of what is commonly referred to as 'the closet' yet and you don't want him exposed as a result of this incident. Am I right?'

Perma-Tan looked up from his papers, winked, and waved a top-secret little dinky wave in my direction.

'Oh, erm, yes. Yes, I'm afraid you're right,' I admitted, taking Perma-Tan's lead. 'Look, does he have to be involved in this? This is really awkward you know.' As I delivered this cringe-making line, I felt something deep in my soul shrivel up and die.

Baldy eyed me square-on. 'Look, Mr Eve, I couldn't care less what you and your chums get up to in bed. The only thing that concerns me is if you are a fugitive on the run. Once we've proved or disproved your story, you will either be free to go or locked up, accordingly. Personally, I think you're telling me the truth, I have to say. No convict would be so stupid as to try to board a plane for Singapore in handcuffs, no offense.'

'None taken,' I assured him, picking up my imaginary shovel. Perma-Tan glared daggers at the back of Baldy's head and then flashed the briefest of sweet smiles at me, before making his excuses and leaving. Thank goodness he knew what was going on, vis-à-vis my covert operation, and had very cleverly fed me the lines to help get me off the hook.

I was then taken through a back door by Mungo and Jerry, down to a bleak, Spartan holding cell, where I was to wait until things were hopefully cleared up. Comically, they informed me that they were supposed to handcuff me, but the logistics of that became too much for either of us to get our heads around, so they decided not to bother. The room had one of those awful little observation hatches where coppers spy on their charges, just in case they decide to hang themselves with their bootlaces out of desperation. Inside, there was a bunk with a thin sheet on top of it, a rancid, sweat-stained pillow, and that was it. I was expecting at least a vase of daffs and a Constable print, just to lighten the mood. God, it was bleak. As I sat there, head in hands, I kept thinking about my cosy flat and my faithful hound, Len. Then I imagined my children weeping for me, and I have to confess, I was so low, I may have shed a tear myself. It seemed like hours that I had been incarcerated, and I had almost certainly missed my flight.

Eventually, the door swung open and Baldy appeared with an envelope in his hand. He told me that my credentials had been verified and that I was free to go. I asked about my flight and he explained that, as I had arrived three hours early and my incarceration had only lasted an hour and a half in total, there was still time to get on the plane, though I might be pushing it if I wanted to get myself some breakfast. He handed me the envelope and told me to present it to customs in Singapore. Unfortunately, there was no one available to remove my cuffs at such short notice, so he had hastily composed an official letter from British customs asking for permission to allow me through without hindrance. There was another for New Zealand if need be, he added, but it would be better all round if, on arriving in Singapore, I headed for the nearest hardware store and invested in a hacksaw.

I thanked him brokenly, grabbed my smelly backpack and ran to gate thirty-six, my handcuffs shoved up my sleeve.

Ten minutes later, I breathlessly boarded the huge jumbo jet and stowed my precious cargo in the locker above my head. I even allowed myself a wry smile at the chaos I had put myself through, even before I'd set foot on the plane, but then the cabin crew began to close the doors, the captain began playing with his engines and I began to panic. I tried to calm myself, taking deep breaths into the sick bag, much to the annoyance of the lady sat beside me. Spotting that I was in need of assurance, an air hostess came over to see me and asked if I was okay. I have to report that I felt a whole lot better when I looked up at her beautiful oriental face. It seemed to calm me down instantly. I sheepishly explained that I was a nervous flyer and she vowed to personally look after me. Meanwhile, I just continued to gaze at her perfect face and drool. I gathered that she was hoping for some sort of response, however minimal, so I snapped out of my reverie and attempted to reply. I deliberately lowered my voice so that, to my mind at least, it had the timbre of Sean Connery, rather than my usual squeaky Jasper Carrott, but I was so mesmerised that I just blurted out a pile of utter gibberish. I'd tell you what I said, but I honestly can't remember. I think my mind has deliberately wiped the tape, as it tends to do with most of my cringeworthy episodes. If she thought I was a complete fool, she didn't show it. She just smiled sweetly and moved on to the next basket case. I glanced around the plane and spotted at least six more of these oriental visions, all more or less identical of face and body. All size eight, maximum, all small breasted, which I find very stimulating, all smiling sweetly, like mine had been, and all breathtakingly perfect. It was as if Singaporeans poured their future air hostesses into some form of mould as children, whence they emerge fully-formed and identical aged twenty-two. A bit like fitting youngsters with braces to ensure their teeth are all perfect in later life, but more radical. The thing that impressed me was the attitude. Call me naïve, but every single one of these girls seemed to be *genuinely* lovely, unlike those British ones you come across, with their cosmetics-counter artificial faces and their phoney smiles that hide a thinly-veiled contempt for the passengers they serve. Not that I blame them for that, by the way, far from it. If I had to deal with some of the ratbags they have to serve on a daily basis, I'd be the same, if not much worse. I've been on a few flights where some of the passengers deserved to be wearing their food, not eating it.

I tried to get comfortable and flicked through the airline magazine, but none of it was sinking in. I preferred to dreamily follow the progress of my personal hostess as she floated around the cabin, dispensing sweetness and light. I tried to imagine her naked, lying on silken sheets, waiting for me in my Singapore hotel room. I would arrive, tired and soaked in sweat and grime after my flight, and she would silently undress me and bathe my body, kissing it here and there as she did so, occasionally whispering in my ear in a language I couldn't understand. Maybe she was explaining her fee structure, but I like to think she was declaring her undying love. Feeling a little hot under the collar now, I removed my coat and placed it in my overhead locker. Unfortunately, in so doing I had somehow managed to unbutton my sleeve and partially roll it up my arm, giving the lady next to me a great view of my handcuff. She quickly averted her gaze, but to my horror she now seemed to be fixated on the crotch area of my jeans, which, to my utter embarrassment, appeared to be hiding a baguette. A petite baguette, admittedly, but even a small hotdog roll can look quite intimidating when placed at a jaunty angle in a tightish pair of Levi's. I had been aware of certain stirrings whilst fantasizing about my night of passion with the air hostess, but I had no idea that I was in such an advanced state of arousal.

As if things weren't embarrassing enough, the lady, who looked a little like my old Headmistress, summoned the object of my desires and frostily demanded she be moved elsewhere. I could have died, I really could. I glared down at my in-flight magazine, which I was using to cover up my wayward member, and pretended to be interested in a Pierre Cardin cigarette lighter with a compass and a digital clock displaying ten different time-zones built into it. The Headmistress shuffled past me, giving me the look of death and me avoiding all eye contact. Ten minutes later, Geisha was back, sweet as ever, but politely requesting a quiet word back at her sleeping quarters. Ordinarily, this would have been enough to set off the hair-trigger on my reproductive equipment and render me a spent force, but something told me – and call me astute if you will – that she wasn't about to suggest that I joined the Mile High Club. We were still on the ground for a start, but you know what I mean. She had a few questions she needed answers to, before the pilot got going. I reached up to the overhead luggage compartment and extricated my letter from Manchester customs, before following meekly behind her to the area where the hostesses took a rest in-between duties. I could see she was feeling uncomfortable about what she had to say to me, so I pre-empted her by handing her the letter.

'I, erm, know why you've asked me down here,' I stammered, my cheeks reddening. 'This letter should explain things. I know the alarm bells would have gone off when that lady asked to be moved after spotting the handcuffs. It's only natural she was alarmed – I would have been for goodness sake! I just need you to know that I'm not some dangerous escaped criminal and you're quite safe to take off.'

Geisha politely acknowledged my comments as she digested the contents of my letter. She returned it and smiled sweetly, maintaining eye contact throughout in a most disconcerting way.

'And I think you need some form of explanation about, you know, the other thing. I, erm, went to a party last night – a friend's leaving party it was – and someone spiked my drink with, erm, Viagra, I think it must have been.'

'Really?' asked Geisha, still burning holes in my retinas with her wonderful, soulful eyes.

Now, my cheeks reddened to Gas Mark Nine (240°C for those with an electric oven). I struggled on regardless.

'It sounds funny,' I continued, my Sean Connery impersonation now discarded and with old Jasper back in charge, 'but it's been deeply embarrassing for me, I can tell you. I don't blame that lady next to me at all. If I'd have been in her shoes, I'd have done the same. The thing is, you see, it keeps going stiff on me whenever I see a lovely woman, or even think about anything a little bit, you know. I can't control it. I daresay it'll subside eventually. They reckon it lasts for twenty-four hours don't they, not that I'm an expert, as I don't take the stuff, obviously, being a normal young man with everything, you know, functioning as it should. I just want to apologize to you and the lady, that's all. It must have sent her over the edge, seeing a bloke in handcuffs with a big erection sitting next to her like that. She probably thought I was an escaped rapist or something. Did she want to get you to throw me off the flight? I'm sure that I ...'

Geisha interrupted me at this juncture by placing her beautifully manicured index finger on her exquisite lips.

'The lady did see the handcuffs and thought it best to ask my advice,' she said, 'but your letter seems to explain everything, so no need to involve the captain I think. She never said anything to me about your erection though, but thank you for telling me all about it. Maybe she was secretly flattered that you found her attractive, even if it was as a result of the Viagra. Now, excuse me, because I must get the plane ready for take-off.'

And with that hammer blow, she floated off to help an old man with his seat belt.

I staggered back to my seat, seriously contemplating spending the entire voyage hidden inside the hand luggage compartment, such was my shame. Instead, I dug out my paperback and retreated into my shell. At least, when the time came to have a nap, I'd have a spare seat to lie across. Every cloud has a silver lining I suppose. I hoped the Headmistress was now sat next to a fat bloke who had B.O., halitosis and flatulence. By Singapore, she'd be begging Geisha to sit her next to the rapist with the stiffy again.

The mighty jumbo ambled along to its starting point, halted for a while and then gave us all a taste of its awesome, stomach-churning power by revving up the mighty Rolls Royce engines. Seconds later, it was belting down the runway and I was busy reading the same line over and over again, clutching my book with sweating palms. They say that, in theory, a bumble bee shouldn't be able to fly, given its shape, weight and wingspan, and in my humble opinion, neither should a jumbo jet. I was just so grateful that I was proved wrong. After what seemed like an hour, it finally hauled itself into the air, and we all said goodbye to dull old Manchester.

I sat staring at the ceiling now and meditating furiously, having abandoned all hope of trying to read my book. The plane eventually levelled, the seatbelt signs pinged, and suddenly, as if from nowhere, Geisha was once more at my side, asking if I was okay. I nodded nervously, trying my best to look meek, vulnerable and unassuming. I've heard that a lot of women prefer that to the recently escaped, criminally insane, over-sexed pervert look.

'I've never flown this far,' I told her. 'I'm dreading it.'

'It's a long journey,' she admitted, 'but it does go quite quickly. By the time you've eaten breakfast, read the papers, dozed off, watched a film, had a drink, eaten lunch, watched a film, dozed off, watched a film, eaten your complimentary peanuts, read your paperback, popped to the loo to freshen up, eaten dinner, watched a film and dozed off again, you'll be almost a quarter of the way there!'

I thanked her brokenly for her words of encouragement. My trouble, I explained, was that I didn't sleep too well if I wasn't in my own bed. Even with the Headmistress's spare seat and the vacant one next to the window, I was likely to wake up as stiff as a board, if I slept at all. Geisha smiled her sweetest smile yet, adding that she hoped I didn't get so stiff as to make the journey frustrating. She then handed me a blow-up pillow to support my neck, a set of headphones, a pair of purple socks and one of those lovely hot towels that look like microwaved spring rolls. I asked her what the socks were for, and she explained that they helped to prevent deep-vein thrombosis. This may or may not have been true, but they certainly helped to prevent attracting a girlfriend, unless of course she was partially-sighted. As I had no one to talk to now that my neighbour had seen fit to emigrate to Row 46, I decided to watch a film, so to this end, I untangled the headphones and tried to fit the things into my ears. Everyone else seemed to be able to manage this, but apparently, my ears were not standard issue. I could not, for the life of me, make the damned earpieces stick in my ear holes for any meaningful length of time, and I couldn't stomach the thought of summoning Geisha yet again to do it for me. She already thought I was wildly oversexed and of questionable morality, and I didn't really wish to add moronic to her ever-growing list of adjectives. I looked at my watch – only another thirteen hours to go. I decided to order a glass of red wine. Maybe that would last at least seven hours if I just sipped it. I could also elect to eat one of my complimentary peanuts every half hour. The time would just fly by. It was then that I had a brainwave. I removed the lace of my right shoe and tried it for size around my head, but it was a very short, thin one, and I could only just about make the ends meet. I removed the other lace and tied them together. This time they went around my head leaving easily enough to tie a bow. I pushed the headphones back in my ears, and quickly tied the laces around them before they could fall out again. This seemed to do the trick, but it must have left me looking either like a hippy en-route, somewhat belatedly, to the Woodstock festival, or perhaps the Mona Lisa, if the viewer happened to be the partially-sighted lady mentioned previously. My euphoria was, however, short-lived. Within seconds, the laces had slipped and were jamming my eyelids shut. Now I could actually hear the film, which, for your information, was No Country for Old Men, starring Tommy Lee Jones, but I could no longer see it. Geisha arrived at my side as if by magic, and whispered that I had the headphones on back to front, which was the reason they wouldn't stay put. As she sashayed down the aisle, I swear I spotted her tittering to herself and cutely holding her nose in order to try to quell her emotions. Singapore was, by all accounts, ruled with a rod of iron, and I daresay that any hostesses found guilty of sniggering at their idiot passengers could be stripped of their batik uniforms and flogged senseless. Had they been Japanese, they'd have fared even worse. They'd probably have made a game show out of it. Torture and ritual humiliation as entertainment!

I turned my attention to the film, and got lost in it for a couple of hours. I have to report that it was excellent, if a little blood-thirsty, but it was the content of this film that made me think a bit. It all started with old Tommy Lee investigating a gruesome scene in a remote field, strewn with dead Latino-type drug dealers. I must point out at this juncture that I am not anti-Latino; far from it. It's just that the fellows always seem to be mixed up in drug dealing, if we are to believe Hollywood. Anyway, this local redneck type happens to come across this mayhem by accident and helps himself to an attaché case full of drug money, which he reckons will keep him in Jack Daniels, loose women and pick-up trucks until the next century. The only trouble is, he hasn't catered for the tall, floppy-haired, deep-voiced psycho assassin hired to retrieve the stolen case and its contents. All of a sudden, the redneck realizes that he's in too deep, and there ain't no way out. Well, I can't tell you how great this made me feel. I started to fret and panic, and all of a sudden, fifteen hundred pounds sterling seemed a very silly, insignificant reward for all I had to put myself through. Had it not been for the damned handcuffs, I would have sailed through Manchester unhindered, but what if Singapore proved trickier? What if my undercover cop had cried off work that day with a cold, and I was left to fend for myself?

Geisha waltzed past and handed me a helpful leaflet about Singapore, explaining to the unfamiliar traveller its customs, rules and regulations. The headline stated:

Singapore has a 'zero tolerance' stance on drugs. The penalty for smuggling can be the death penalty, or else life imprisonment.

I re-read the headline, just to make sure I hadn't misunderstood. Suddenly, I was aware of something pounding furiously in my mouth. It was my heart, trying to vacate the premises. My vision began to swim. I could see two TV screens in the back of my seat, and two sick bags dancing in my lap. What on earth had I got myself into? I wanted to grab Geisha and explain to her what I was going through. Surely she'd understand. I'd already bared my soul to her about being handcuffed and having an erection, so an admission that I was a novice heroin smuggler would be like water off a duck's back to her now. She'd probably just smile sweetly and totter off to get me a hookah pipe to suck on.

What was I saying? There was no way I could just own up and expect to be absolved of all my sins. I'd already gone way too far for that, now that my stash was hidden in the suitcase in the hold. They'd shoot me anyway, or hang me, or send me to the electric chair, or whatever the Singaporeans did to those who were surplus to requirements. I felt very clammy and cold all of a sudden, even though the cabin was too hot. My peripheral vision seemed to be getting darker and darker, like a camera lens being stopped down to F22. After that, you'll have to ask the elderly couple in the next aisle what happened. I was no longer amongst those conscious.

When I came round, I was met by the most beautiful pair of oriental eyes, around a foot away from my face. Geisha was dabbing a cold towel on my fevered brow and asking if I was alright. I was informed later on that my first words, upon regaining consciousness, were, 'I'd prefer to be shot, if you wouldn't mind.'

Thankfully, she took this as merely the delirious ramblings of a man who had just re-surfaced after passing out. She asked if I had a medical condition, and I assured her that I was okay, adding that my faint was possibly caused by worrying about my first long-haul flight, the hot cabin and the fact that I hadn't eaten. She explained that food would be arriving shortly, if only certain passengers would refrain from wearing handcuffs, having erections, tying shoe laces around their heads and fainting, all of which hindered her progress with the trolley. I toyed with the idea of stripping naked and shitting in the aisle whilst playing the bagpipes. Then she'd have the full set. I'd even stopped blushing now. I think my blushing censors had just gone way into the red and fused, leaving me completely desensitized.

I vowed to become low-profile for the rest of the trip; to blot out any thoughts of drug smuggling, execution or handcuffs. I would simply shut them out of my mind, relax, enjoy the flight, the films and the food, follow my progress on-screen with the red line snaking across the world map, and try to sleep when the time came. There was no point in worrying about something I couldn't change, so I didn't. I switched off.

I spent an interminable night beneath a thin and ineffectual tartan rug (supplied with a smile by a seemingly indefatigable Geisha) listening to the elderly gentleman in the middle aisle snoring like a pot-bellied pig. I swear one more hour of it would have resulted in homicide. How his wife coped, I will never know. I briefly toyed with removing my stylish purple sock and stuffing it down his wide-open, spittle-filled mouth, but I could ill-afford another incident.

I had now spent two nights wide-awake, and I was becoming seriously addled with sleep deprivation. I was so desperately tired and bored that I actually began to look forward to visiting the lavatory, just for something to do. While I waited my turn for the umpteenth time, I observed Geisha and her colleagues administering to the needy and the sick, the hungry and the thirsty, and the drained young parents trying to cope with screaming infants in cots. It was a vision of purgatory, but she was like an oriental Florence Nightingale, holding us all together in times of stress. Maybe it was the delirium kicking in, but I even suspected that she could be a highly sophisticated android, like in the film Blade Runner. What other reason could be offered to explain the fact that she never seemed to require sleep, food or toilet breaks? Her constant cheerful nature, politeness and patience were surely not hallmarks of the human being. Did she occasionally slip back to some private room to swear, smoke, scowl, fart and gorge on sausage rolls or crack cocaine, I wondered, or did she only need to return there in order to plug something into her side which recharged her Duracell batteries in time for the next shift?

I slipped into the tiny lavatory and bolted the door. Looking back at me was a grey-skinned, unshaven zombie with baggy, bloodshot eyes and greasy hair sticking out in unkempt tufts. Right now, even the promise of nearly a quarter of a million pounds didn't seem like enough. I splashed water on my face and dried it with a paper towel, leaving hundreds of bits of green soggy paper stuck to my stubble. Somewhere outside, an intercom announced that we should return to our seats. This had happened several

69

times during the journey due to turbulence, but this time the message was different. Somehow, the pilot had managed to guide a colossal tube of metal full of highly-strung people halfway round the world, often in total darkness at thirty-five thousand feet, and now he was endeavouring to bring it down and land it on a runway measuring no more than a few yards across. Oh joy of joys! We were finally there, or thereabouts, and for one tired, forlorn, sweaty, shattered individual, it hadn't come a moment too soon. I sat down and strapped myself in. Then, after making sure that no one was looking, I reached across and poked Mr Snorer really hard in the arm and then quickly pretended to be engrossed in my paperback. He awoke with an impressive yelp, glanced around him in a distracted way and then smiled at me.

'Sorry,' he said shakily, 'I must have been having a bad dream.'

'Don't apologize!' I smiled, 'I have them all the time. In fact, I'm having one now!'

72

CHAPTER 6

In which I am rather glad that I asked for a 'no smoking' room.

The stewards opened the cabin doors front and back. It felt similar to when I once opened my oven door and looked inside to check on the progress of a Waitrose chicken and ham pie, momentarily forgetting that the oven was set to Gas Mark Nine. As a result I exited sharply with peeling skin and steamed-up glasses, like the ones Mr Magoo used to wear. Boy, Singapore was hot, and so humid, I could barely breathe. There was no point rushing, and I was damned if I was going to fight it out with all the others to get to the overhead lockers first, so I just sat there dazed. Geisha helped Mr and Mrs Pot-Bellied Snorer to retrieve their bags and then she turned to me and asked how I was feeling. I tried as hard as I could to look like a lost, eight-week-old Cavalier King Charles Spaniel puppy, and replied that I was okay, thank you. I added some self-pitying remark about being all alone in a big, strange city, and about how I'd had more than enough mishaps to last me a lifetime. Then, out of nowhere, I asked her.

I must confess that I have never, ever, ever, chatted up a girl in my life. I am far too thin-skinned to cope with a rejection for starters. A mate of mine recently tried it on with a much younger woman in the typing pool at his place of work.

'Would you like to come for a coffee this lunchtime?' he'd asked feebly.

'Why?' she had replied, nonplussed.

73

Well, that would have killed me stone dead. I wouldn't have known how to respond. If a woman hadn't made the first move on every occasion, I'd never have had a single girlfriend, or eventually, a wife. It was then, a complete surprise to me when I heard myself coyly asking Geisha if she had any time off, now that she was in Singapore, and would she care to join me for lunch once we'd both had a good night's sleep. She flushed ever so slightly and smiled.

'I don't think my partner would be too happy if I did,' she explained, pointing in the general direction of a steward at the other end of the cabin, busy collecting up the headphones.

'Oh, I'm sorry,' I groaned. 'I didn't realize. I naturally thought that he was, well, you know, gay. It's a well-known fact that everyone that works on these airlines is…'

'Queer?'

'Well yes.'

'He is,' smiled Geisha. 'You were right. But I wasn't referring to him. I was pointing to the lady collecting up the purple socks, next to him.'

*****

Having sailed through passport control, I stood by the carousel waiting for my luggage, hanging onto the trolley in order to prevent myself from falling down. I spent most of the time until my suitcase arrived pondering the unfairness of life. I remember my ex-wife, Katie, saying that Julian Clary was such a waste, because he was so beautiful, and yet so utterly useless to her. Well this is how I was feeling about Geisha. She was the perfect woman, apart from one small but significant detail. Men didn't do it for her. At least, in her defence, she was in love with another beautiful woman, so in that respect, she was a true lesbian, which I

74

begrudgingly respected. What I could never understand were the ones who tried to look like men. If you will recall, in the typical lesbian partnership, there is usually a feminine-looking one and a masculine-looking one. This has never made sense to me. Surely, if they are attracted to their own sex, why is it that one of them deems it necessary to act and dress like a man? Are they not then admitting that a male partner is the ideal? If I were gay, would I not be attracted to someone who looked like a bloke, rather than a woman? Call me naïve if you will, but I don't get it.

I would have gone into this more deeply, but it was then that I saw my blue case trundling along on the conveyor belt, so I had to act quickly. I hauled it off and lifted it onto the trolley, took a deep breath to fortify myself and headed for the customs area, trying to look nonchalant and missing it by a mile. For starters, I hadn't got a clue where I was supposed to be looking. If I looked at the officers and met their gaze, that could be troublesome. If I avoided eye contact, it could be even worse, and if I whistled a jaunty tune, I might as well have resigned myself to the firing squad. It wouldn't have been so bad had I travelled with my family. Then I could have chatted breezily to my daughter or son, like the good, solid, dependable dad I was. Instead, I felt as guilty as a fox in a henhouse, and I was sure they could smell the fear from ten paces away. That and the body odour caused by spending fourteen hours in a plane.

I decided on a middle-of-the-road approach. As I walked past, legs like jelly, I smiled sweetly but briefly at the three diminutive officers on duty. Three or four steps to go, and I was out of there, free as a bird. Then one of them said, 'Excuse me, sir,' and my anal sphincter tightened. I turned to face them, my heart pounding furiously.

'Y-yes?' I stammered.

'Could you just step to one side, please?'

I did as I was told. The one in the middle addressed me.

'I hope you don't mind, sir, but my friend here has seen all your films. Could you sign book for him, please? I am asking because his Engrish nosso good.'

I swallowed hard, and smiled again.

'Erm, how do you want me to sign it?' I asked nervously.

There was a brief discussion in what I presumed was Chinese, though I'm no expert.

'He says, 'To Marco, best wishes, Nichoras Cage' will be fine.'

I borrowed his pen and wrote exactly that, with trembling hand, for which they thanked me profusely. In a sudden flash of inspiration, I slipped on my free-with-the-toothpaste RayBans (to give me the Hollywood look), casually saluted them in that nauseating American way, and then aimed my wayward trolley for the wide-open spaces at a rate of knots.

Thankful though I was, I still wasn't clear about who, if anyone, had eased my passage through customs. Had my stash of heroin simply gone undetected, or had someone let it through on the nod? Maybe it was no longer residing in my luggage, and the three Stooges had got it. If they had, did they think they'd purloined it from a Hollywood star travelling under an assumed name? As usual, there were far too many questions and not enough answers. The best thing to do was to hail a cab and head for the Merlion Hotel, Clarke Quay, where I could take a look for myself. It was here that my contact would relieve me of my responsibilities, unless, of course, someone hadn't already done that back at the airport.

I must say that I was impressed with Singapore. I'd gone past the tiredness stage now, though I was sure that once I saw my hotel bed it would come back. Meanwhile, I felt surprisingly awake and able to take in what I was seeing as I whizzed through the busy early morning streets in my bright yellow taxi. Tina from the travel firm had been spot-on too. The taxi drivers, if mine was anything to go by, *were* extremely friendly and chatty. *Too* chatty for those who weren't at their best after whole days spent travelling I suspect, but I could cope, and it would have seemed churlish to sit in the back and blank him out.

The first thing that confused me was the name of the place. I hadn't realized, until my driver informed me, that the capital city *and* the country were both called Singapore. I couldn't understand the reasoning behind this, unless the government had introduced name rationing during the war. Either that, or perhaps, when they were designing the map of their country, the cartographers had intended to call the capital city something different, like Ping Ho Ding Chong, for example, but by that time they'd used up most of their Letraset so they couldn't. Then, one bright spark must have noticed that the few characters they had left would just about spell Singapore if they used an upside down 'd' for the 'p', so rather than buy a new sheet, they decided on that instead. Yes, that must be it. I can't think of any other reason for it.

I expected to find myself in a ramshackle place with filthy back streets that resembled rabbit warrens, but the city centre was more like Dallas, with huge, brand-new sky-scrapers, palm trees, trendy apartments and beautiful floral arrangements in the central reservations of dual carriageways. Back in England, by sharp contrast, we tend to go for Kentucky Fried Chicken and McDonalds take-away box arrangements, interspersed with vomit. I must admit to feeling a little homesick when I began to make comparisons. By this, I mean that I suddenly became extremely sick of my home. I noted with interest there was no litter – not even in the less salubrious areas – and the distinctive white blobs of chewing gum that disfigure our English streets were conspicuous by their absence. I was told by William, my Chinese-looking driver with the curiously English name, that vandalism was punished with the birch, chewing gum was completely forbidden, and violent crime meant a life-sentence. I couldn't help thinking that England got what it deserved, on hearing all this. We've effectively been sparing the rod and spoiling the child for years, and now the chickens were coming home to roost, and they were wearing hoodies.

My taxi took me past Little India – which looked less well-heeled, like I imagined the tidier streets of Bombay would look – and China Town, which was very colourful and lively, with alleys full of bustling market stalls. I made a mental note to visit the place once I'd had a good sleep. Then we pulled up outside a very smart new development full of trendy shops, restaurants and bars, which led to the river. This was Clarke Quay, and my hotel, the Merlion, was just across the road. I thanked William and offered him a modest tip that he politely refused. I tried to foist it on him as reward for my guided tour, and yet again he refused, advising me to spend it on a coffee at the hotel instead. I asked if all the Singapore drivers were as polite, and he informed me that they were simply not allowed to take tips. Assuring him that what took place between the two of us in his cab was strictly private and would go no further, I tried again, only to be met with a firm but friendly rebuttal. Reluctantly, I put the coins back in my pocket, and he helped me to unload my bags. How different he was to the London cab driver who picked me up at Euston train station a few years back, took his instructions and promptly dropped me off all of twenty yards down the road in return for his exorbitant minimum fare. How was I supposed to know that my end destination was actually situated in Euston Square? I don't live in the God-forsaken hole do I?

No sooner had I vacated the cab, when some sub-species of hotel employee was carting my bags up the steps three at a time, as quick as a flash. The lad looked a bit like an anorexic version of Bruce Lee. He was clearly undernourished and must have only weighed three stone, but he seemed to be able to carry half-ton suitcases with consummate ease. I thanked him profusely – for I was once again beginning to wilt – and slipped him a few quid in the local coinage, which he snatched like they were going out of fashion. What you win on the taxis, you lose on the porters, I always say. Well, that's not strictly true – I've never said it in my life, but I'll be saying it regularly from now on, that's for sure, even if no one understands what I'm on about. I proceeded to the glitzy marbled reception area, my entire body now buzzing with severe sleep deprivation. I admit that 'buzzing' doesn't sound like the right adjective, but I can assure you that it was. It was like a gentle electrical hum, to be more precise. The uniformed character behind the desk asked me to fill in a long, tedious form – which I just love doing when I'm jet-lagged and delirious – and then informed me that my room number was 607, but it wasn't ready yet (surprise, surprise), as it was still only nine-thirty in the morning. He said that I would have to wait an hour, or I could have the smoking room – number 606, next door. I reluctantly accepted, grabbed the key card, politely refused Anorexic Bruce Lee's offer of assistance on the grounds that he'd fleeced me quite enough for one day, and summoned the lift.

Silly as it seems, I always get this little frisson of excitement before entering a new hotel room. I shoved the key card in and swiped it, and was rather pleased to see the little green light which meant that my attempt at entry had been successful. This made a nice change, because nineteen times out of twenty I can't work the things properly. I shoved the door open and dragged my belongings in behind me, quickly scanning the room to see how big it was, what my bed was like; the usual stuff. It all looked fine, and more than adequate for a quick one-night stay. Looks, though, aren't everything, as we all know. Smell is quite important too, and this room smelt as if the previous occupant had been smoking a haddock in there. Jeez, it stunk awful. My guess was that the Merlion Hotel had recently played host to the Far East Pipe-Man of the Year contest. Either that or Anorexic Bruce Lee had been using it as an opium den during his breaks. I opened the windows, which immediately let in the cacophony of Singapore's never-ending traffic. I didn't know which was worse, to be truthful, but I decided to put up with it for ten minutes, until the worst of the Old Shag had dissipated. Meanwhile, I hauled my blue suitcase onto the shelf provided and impatiently fiddled with the keys until the locks were opened. I clicked the two catches and lifted the lid, as eagerly as a little boy desperate to see what Santa had bought him. A strange analogy I admit, considering what I was searching for, but it was wrapped in festive paper, after all.

I threw the top layer of garments, underpants and assorted socks onto the adjoining dresser in a frenzy, and there it was, exactly as I'd packed it – Aunt Jemima's Christmas present. The police would be pleased. This meant that no one, at least this time around, had been filching the white stuff. Now all I had to do was try to sleep for a few hours, until the time came to be rudely awoken by my undercover contact, claiming his goods. Then I'd be free to enjoy the rest of my holiday without that horrible little black cloud hovering over me. I threw off my shoes and socks (which crawled under the bed unaided), stripped down to my boxers, closed the window to shut out the traffic noise and collapsed onto my bed. God, it was heaven! I don't know if you've ever had a general (a general anaesthetic I mean – I wasn't probing into your militaristic sexual preferences), but if you have, you'll know that they stick a little needle into your hand and ask you to count to ten, and before you can get to three, you're asleep. Well, that was how quickly I dropped off. Even my cumbersome and uncomfortable handcuffs couldn't prevent me from sleeping this time; I was so pooped.

It was two in the afternoon when I resurfaced, and that, too, was slow and painstaking, like coming out from under the ether after an operation. I lay there staring at the ceiling for what seemed like hours, unable to move a muscle. Eventually, with supreme effort, I dragged myself into the shower. Had I not forced myself to do so I know I would have gone under again and woken up at three in the morning, my body clock completely out of kilter.

The warm water did wonders. After a luxuriant fifteen minutes of ecstatic groaning, I dried myself and put on some fresh clothes, ready to explore the city. Ideally, in Singapore's eighty-five degree heat and strength-sapping humidity, I needed to be wearing a short-sleeved shirt with my shorts, but this would have exposed my cuffs. Reluctantly, I pulled on a lightweight jumper, grabbed my room key and wallet and made for the door. Then it dawned on me that my police contact had not yet been to see me. I suppose I should have stayed holed up in my room, but I really wanted to go out and do a bit of sight-seeing. It wasn't every day one wound up in such an interesting place and time was precious, as I was leaving the following afternoon. I decided to inform the concierge that I was popping out to explore, and if anyone wished to see me, he was to let them know my room number and ask them to call back at six.

I walked through the cool, marble-clad lobby, out of the front doors, into the blistering heat, and it took my breath away. How on earth did these people function in such ferocious temperatures, I wondered. I made a mental note to locate the boffin who invented air conditioning and thank him personally, if he was still with us. Luckily, the Singapore taxis all seemed to have air-con that a fridge-freezer wouldn't have been ashamed of, so I got Anorexic Bruce Lee to hail me one and piled in. My driver, Henry (what was it with their English names?), was another affable fellow who took me to a huge, and I mean HUGE, store called the Mustapha Centre, which sold virtually everything with the exception of maybe musical false teeth. Everything else, they had in stock, and I'm sure that they could have ordered the musical false teeth if you were desperate for a set. There were hundreds of escalators leading to floor after floor after floor, and the place was open twenty-four hours a day. I was fascinated. The electrical goods and photographic equipment seemed to be far cheaper than in England – well, there's a surprise – but this was not just an oversized Curry's or Dixon's. There were whole aisles of luggage, a deli the size of Wolverhampton, sports equipment and clothing, whole floors full of jewellery and watches, acres of pet food and miles of cheap shirts – you name it, it was there somewhere if you had enough years left in you to search. I hadn't flown all that way to look around a department store, however. I was a man on a mission. I scanned the signage and located the hardware department on the seventh floor, next to the spare parts for space shuttles.

Fifteen minutes later, I was out on the baking-hot street again clutching my hacksaw. I hailed a cab and asked the driver to take me back to the hotel, pronto. I'd lived like an escaped fugitive for two days now, and that, I can assure you, was more than enough.

I strode purposefully up to the reception desk and tried to spot the man I had dealt with earlier, but I was informed that he had finished his shift for the day. His colleague introduced himself and asked if he could be of assistance. I explained that I was expecting a visitor, and asked if anyone had been asking for me.

'Ah, yes!' said the new boy. 'Two gentlemen came to the desk and asked if you were in, and I passed on the message that you had gone sight-seeing and would be back at six, I believe you said. They asked which room you were staying in. I told them it was 607. I hope you don't mind, but you did say you were expecting them.'

'That's fine,' I replied, 'but I'm not in 607 any more. Your colleague said the room wasn't ready when I arrived and I was desperate for a sleep, so he put me next door in 606, the room where you usually put people with a ninety-a-day habit.'

The new concierge had the look of a person who was not quite getting the gist. I decided not to pursue it.

'I didn't realize you'd been moved, Mr Eve,' he explained. 'I had you down as Room 607. It's absolutely no problem, but the two gentlemen did say that they were going to pop up to your room and slip an envelope under your door. I said that this was okay, but obviously, now your next-door neighbour will have the note instead of you. Maybe I'll go with you to the room and retrieve it for you. I happen to know that the gentleman is German and, unusually, speaks no English, so maybe it's easier if I do it!'

I thanked him and added that I hoped I wasn't causing him too much trouble. We caught the lift and he asked me what the hacksaw was for. I explained that I was an escaped criminal, and I intended to cut off my handcuffs with it. He found this very amusing indeed. I've found, over the years, that it is possible to say absolutely anything to anyone, and as long as you grin inanely as you say it, no one bats an eyelid. We reached the door of 607 and my friend rapped it gently. There was no reply. He tried again, this time with gusto. Still nothing.

He slipped his master key card into the slot and swiped it.

'I just hope he's not in bed, snoring, or making love, or even worse, deaf and shitting,' he added. I shuddered at the prospect. I could take deaf, and I could even put up with shitting, but not both. We entered the room, which was extremely dark, due to the blinds being closed. The concierge flicked the light switch and looked on the floor, but there was no letter. It was then that he noticed the limp, bare leg hanging off the end of the bed at the other end of the room. He crept across to take a look, leaving me waiting at the doorway. Then he doubled up and vomited out the remains of his lunch.

FU MANCHU

FOR MAYOR

THIS ADVERTISEMENT WAS PAID FOR BY THE CITIZENS COMMITTEE TO ELECT FU MANCHU FOR MAYOR

CHAPTER 7

In which I meet Fu Manchu for the first time.

Herr Fuchs didn't look well. In fact, he looked as unwell as a German scissor-lift crane salesman could look. He was dead, or, as he would have put it, had he been able to, 'Ich bin tot'.

The concierge had recovered sufficiently to ring reception and ask for the police and an ambulance straight away, and now it was my turn to be off-colour. I'd always been a bit sceptical about this 'throwing up immediately upon sight of a dead body' thing. Whenever a corpse is discovered in crime thrillers, the young rookie copper always goes green instantly and pukes into his helmet, whilst the seasoned older detective, who's seen it all before, gets on with the ghastly business of examining the body. I always took this to be a bit of artistic licence, a stock response that film-makers use to get over the point. I can now report that I was wrong. I took one look at the poor unfortunate victim and added to the chamber maid's woes in prolific fashion. You see, this wasn't a common-or-garden heart attack, caused by spending too many years in hotel rooms, eating too many fatty room service hamburgers. That was bad enough, but unless I'm very much mistaken, high cholesterol didn't usually manifest itself as a deeply slit throat. Nor did it rummage through one's bags and turn everything upside down afterwards, out of spite. That said, it wasn't *just* the sight of a murdered, overweight German sales rep and his soggy red duvet that got me projectile vomiting in the style made fashionable by Linda Blair in The Exorcist. It was the realization that, unless I was very much mistaken, this scene of carnage was meant for me. We vacated the scene of the crime pronto, locked up and caught the lift down to the concierge's office, where half a dozen staff and the hotel manager were already waiting for us. We were sat down, counselled and generally fussed over, while some acne-scarred lackey was despatched to get tea. As I sat there, nervous as hell, my teacup and saucer clattering together like a pantomime horse's hooves and tea spilling all over the place, I suddenly realized that I still hadn't had chance to remove my handcuffs, such was the pace of my social life. As if that wasn't bad enough, now the manager was asking probing questions about the man or men I was expecting a visit from. He seemed to find it intriguing that two gentlemen had called by asking for me, and upon hearing that I was out, popped up to what they thought was my room to leave a letter which was never found. Well, to be honest, I hadn't a clue how to respond to this, and he was waiting for an answer, so I replied in somewhat woolly fashion:

'Ah, it's a long story, but basically....'

Well, I didn't have the foggiest idea what I was going to say next, but luckily the door burst open at this juncture, and in walked a senior police officer and a young rookie cop who looked as if he were about to faint; I have seen frogs that were less green. This bought me a few precious seconds, and like the graceful swan I shook hands with the senior police officer and introduced myself (if indeed swans are capable of shaking hands). Meanwhile, under the surface, I was paddling furiously. Had I actually been a swan, I reckon I would have been doing at least fifty miles per hour down the Severn, and churning up the water like a jet boat.

I allowed the hotel manager to explain what had happened, because it allowed me the precious extra time to concoct a story. Now it was the police officer's turn to probe me. It was obvious to the meanest intelligence that these two mystery gentlemen had to be regarded as potential suspects, and it was also a distinct possibility that it was me that they were after, and not the unfortunate scissor-lift salesman. The spotty-faced lackey who had earlier been sent to bring tea was now sent in search of CCTV evidence, and in the meantime I was expected to tell all, omitting no detail however slight, beginning with the names and addresses of my visitors and the reason for their visit.

I often use the expression, 'Out of Desperation Cometh Inspiration' and once more this had proved to be true. In the two minutes it had taken the manager to explain why his once respectable hotel now resembled a giant Cluedo board, I had come up with a workmanlike, if not inspired response. Taking a fortifying gulp of tea, which went down the wrong way and nearly choked me to death, I let them have it, such as it was. I was, I explained to my rapt audience, en route to New Zealand with a very rare and expensive Maori carving, in order that the museum in Rotorua could give me an estimate of its worth, and maybe even purchase the thing. I told the policeman that I had been left the item in my uncle's will, and, having no immediate need for an ugly lump of wood with mother of pearl eyes and an angry grimace, had decided to swap it for cash, which I always had a need for. Having blurted out this story to all and sundry in the local hostelries, I was surprised to receive a call from a gentleman who called himself Henry Wong and was potentially interested in acquiring it for his personal collection. (In case you're wondering, I borrowed the name from a small chain of Chinese restaurants in Birmingham. It was the best I could do in a hurry.)

This Mr Wong told me that he lived in Singapore, and had heard about my carving from a friend of a friend who must have been standing at the bar when I was boring everyone rigid with my inheritance story. He asked if he could take a look at the piece on the day I passed through en route to New Zealand, with a view to purchasing same if it took his fancy, before the museum could get their hands on it. He also added that he would pay far more than any museum, being both a dedicated collector and seriously loaded – two attributes I admire in a man. I wrapped up my tale by speculating that this Mr Wong was my mystery visitor, and the other gentleman, if one used the term loosely, was his henchman. I then, rather cleverly in my opinion, offered the policemen an explanation as to how and why Herr Fuchs had been murdered.

'My theory is this,' I began, pacing the room now like Poirot always does in the oak-panelled library when he's about to name his suspect. 'If poor old Herr Fuchs had answered the door, and the two men had bothered with the usual pleasantries, they would have realized that they had the wrong man. However, I believe that they just barged in and accosted him before he could explain that they were in the wrong room. Either that or they had a way of opening the door while he was still in bed, and the man was murdered in his sleep.'

The senior policeman spoke, eyeing me in roughly the same way that a mongoose eyes a snake.

'Very interesting, Mr Eve. You are wasted as a, well, whatever you are...'

'A writer.'

'Oh, well that's blown my next line. In that case, you are not wasted as a writer at all. I was going to say that you were wasted as...'

'As a writer, you should have been a detective.'

'Precisely, but your being a writer makes a nonsense of my joke now, doesn't it? After all, a writer would employ many of the same skills as a detective, especially if he were a crime writer.'

The bloke was beginning to get on my nerves now. His conversation was as dull as ditchwater – so pedantic! I smiled a watery smile and encouraged him to get to the point.

'Do you have this carving with you, Mr Eve?' he asked.

'Yes, it's in my room. Would you like to see it?'

'I would, if you don't mind,' replied the policeman. 'It helps to verify your story.'

The officer, his deputy, the concierge, the manager and I trooped over to the lift and pressed the button for floor six. After a few minutes of stony silence that seemed more like an hour, we spilled out and walked the short distance to my room, passing Herr Fuchs's room, which now had yellow tape across the door and a sign saying, 'Police Investigation – No Entry' in several languages. The concierge opened my door and we piled in. I asked everyone to excuse the state of the place. There was stuff everywhere and I was ashamed of it, to be honest. I opened my hold-all and handed the officer the package containing Mr Maori. He carefully cut it open and took out the carving.

'It doesn't look much of a thing,' he observed. 'You say this is worth a lot of money?'

'Apparently so,' I replied. 'There's no accounting for taste is there?'

'No, Mr Eve, there isn't. Can I ask you, did you pack this yourself? Sometimes we deal with cases where people have been asked to take certain items to other countries, and they turn out to be hollow and filled with drugs. You can't be too careful.'

He tapped it, shook it and listened to it before declaring it a solid object. He picked up Aunt Jemima's present from the bed and handed it to me, so that he could sit down. My heart stopped, and I had to momentarily turn away and whack my chest forcibly to get it going again, in the absence of any electric paddles.

'Please excuse me,' he continued, 'but I had to see your carving with my own eyes and ask the question. The smugglers are getting cleverer week by week. We had a murder only last year at this very hotel, and the victim's wounds were almost identical. That was drug-related. A middle-aged Indian man from Birmingham had been asked to bring to Singapore a large quantity of heroin hidden in a consignment of hollow cricket bats, of all things, in return for a substantial payment. Instead, he had his throat slit. I'm sure he would have preferred the cash. The smugglers are very crafty, and often we police officers feel as if we are fighting a losing battle. We even had a gullible young man from your country in custody recently, who said he was asked to take heroin through customs by, of all things, an English undercover police unit. Apparently, they told him some cock and bull story about suspecting the airport officials of impropriety, and asked him to help with their covert operation to help catch them. Can you believe that anyone could fall for such nonsense?'

I was beginning to feel very giddy indeed. I rammed Aunt Jemima's present back into my suitcase and casually threw a shirt over it, before slumping into the nearest armchair.

'There's one born every minute,' I sighed.

The officer asked if I was okay. Apparently, the blood that usually inhabited my face had left unexpectedly and not left a forwarding address. The man said several other things, but they may as well have been in Chinese; such was the state of turmoil my mind was in. I was vaguely aware of nodding at him every now and again, but nothing was sinking in. I had an awful feeling that I was about to repeat my mid-air fainting routine again, and old Fu Manchu was a very poor second best to Geisha when it came to the kiss of life. Luckily, however, he seemed to be wrapping things up now, if his body language was anything to go by. He stood up, instructed his junior colleague to do likewise, and was heading for the door. With one almighty effort, I stood up to see him out. He told me that a plain-clothed officer would be stationed at the hotel until I left the following day, just in case the two stooges returned. In the meantime, he would examine the CCTV evidence, if there was any, and if anything of significance happened or I had any more leads for them to go on, I was to phone him immediately. He opened the door of my room and walked into the sixth floor corridor, glancing back at me one more time with a concerned look on his usually inscrutable face.

'Are you sure you are okay, Mr Eve? You look white.'

'I'll be fine,' I whimpered. 'I've been travelling for a whole day, I haven't eaten for hours and I haven't slept properly for two days.

90

The man next door has been brutally murdered, and it sounds as if I was the intended victim. I reckon that's enough to make a person go white, don't you?'

Fu Manchu allowed himself a quick smile, which meant he probably wasn't due another one till April. He wrote down my mobile number in case he needed me and led his posse back to the lift. I closed my door and took the hacksaw into the bathroom. It was no more than a few seconds before I realized that it wasn't going to be as easy as I had imagined. For a start, the hand I would have preferably used to hold the saw was the one that had the handcuff attached to it. Then there was the small matter of holding the thing still while I sawed. Ideally, I needed three hands, and having evolved and moved away from my chimp friends over the course of the last few hundred thousand years, my feet were no longer up to it. After much swearing and experimentation, I ended up clasping the cuff between my knees to steady it. This seemed to work after a fashion, but my knees were hardly vice-like, the metal was tough, and the saw kept snagging. It was also dangerously close to my wrist, and my notoriously vivid imagination could envisage a huge spurt of red liquid arcing across the bathroom, followed seconds later by my lifeless body slumping into the bath. The shock of this would surely prove too much for the long-suffering little oriental maid, who'd presumably have to clean up after Herr Fuchs when the police gave her the go-ahead.

I am a quietly determined individual, however, and I persevered. An hour later, cut to pieces and soaked in the sweat of honest toil – if removing handcuffs can be described as honest toil – I gingerly hacked my way through the remaining millimetre of metal. Now I had a handcuff with a fine saw cut running through it that still wouldn't come off my wrist, and two knees with very deep blue-tinged grooves in them. I tried to lever the two separated sections of cuff apart, but the metal was solid, and very tough indeed. I scoured the hotel room, looking for something to wedge into the split so that I could force the two sections apart, but nothing presented itself. Then I noticed the metal bottle opener

91

on a chain, by the mini-bar. I managed to wedge this into the gap, but when I tried to lever the two sections apart, it bent in half and snapped. Now I had two choices. I could cry like a baby, or return to the bathroom with my newly acquired hacksaw and start cutting through the opposite side of the cuff till the middle section fell out. In trying circumstances such as this, many men would have crumbled, but not I. I seem to have deep reserves of patience that I can draw upon, and I tend to adopt a philosophical approach. Indeed, it is the amateur philosopher in me that had rescued me from some pretty dire situations in the past. I say amateur, because, so far, no one has volunteered to pay me to philosophize, and it was this very line of thought that intrigued me and helped pass the time as I embarked upon my second marathon sawing stint. I began to wonder how professional philosophers earned a living – the likes of Plato and Socrates, for example. Did someone simply ring them up and book a full day's philosophizing, after first requesting a quote? Did these philosophers then send an invoice plus V.A.T., worded:

'To supplying one day's worth of deep thinking at your Slough office, plus travel and materials.'

I started to delve deeper into this as I sawed away. Were these philosophers paid by results or was it a daily rate, regardless of how much stuff they managed to think deeply about? Did they have bonus schemes if they came up with something extremely profound, such as the meaning of the universe? Then I began to wonder about them being unemployed. Did they have to get the hours in while they could, knowing that work got a bit slack during the summer when folks were away on holiday? Were they affected by the recession? Was deep thinking dearer of a weekend or after six in the evenings, and was there an emergency call-out price when someone needed some thinking done at short notice? I thought this through logically and decided that, to make ends meet, philosophers probably did other jobs as well. I should imagine that Plato started by dividing his time between thinking and tiling bathrooms, and he only ditched the tiling once he became a superstar, much later on in life when his beard had grown a bit and gone white. I was about to open up a brand new line of enquiry regarding uniforms, trade unions and the like, when all of a sudden I realized that I was down to the last millimetre again and nearly free. This, my friends, is the beauty of deep thinking. Not only does it help pass the time, but it sets you free, not just from imaginary chains, but also from real ones.

I slid my battered wrist carefully between the two jagged edges of metal before diligently cleaning up the hundreds of bits of steel on the bathroom tiles. As I did so, I admired their neat grouting, and wondered to myself if old Plato himself had done it. He was certainly known as a better grouter than Socrates in his day, though Socrates was better at doing around windows. Jeez! I needed food and a good night's sleep. Even *I* could tell that I was becoming delirious, and they reckon you're always the last to know. I lifted the ceramic lid of the toilet cistern and deposited my sawn-up handcuffs inside. Lord knows why I did that. I suppose I must have seen it in films. Didn't Al Pacino retrieve a revolver from a lavatory cistern in that Italian restaurant in the Godfather? Maybe that's where I got it from. I slumped onto my bed and perused the room service menu, deciding on the Chicken sandwich and a bottle of Tiger beer, which I duly ordered. To while away the time, I recovered Aunt Jemima's present from my suitcase and unwrapped it. I opened one of the heroin bags, dipped my finger into it and tasted it. It would never replace the old sherbet dip, in my humble opinion. Then I decided to empty the bags into the lavatory and flush them away. Good riddance, I thought, and surprise surprise: there were no secret tracking devices in any of them. Now all I had to do was survive the night without having my throat cut and hope Fu Manchu managed to capture the two killers before I went sight-seeing again in the morning.

CHAPTER 8

In which I vow to disembowel the very next Chinese camera salesman that I meet.

I awoke at eight, and after a brief check I was able to confirm that I had not been murdered in my sleep, which is always an encouraging start to the day, I reckon. There were no gangsters under my bed, no crazed knifeman behind the shower curtain and no dwarf assassin hiding in the mini-bar. I didn't think there would be really. He'd have been too frozen to kill me anyway after a night spent in there, unless, of course, he'd sneaked in at ten to eight and taken a hot water bottle with him. I showered, dressed, and made my way downstairs, looking over my shoulder nervously at every sudden noise.

The breakfast room was a hive of activity, with large groups of people that looked as if they belonged to an assortment of weird organizations, huddled together in corners. There was a gaggle of loud, brash American students that might or might not have been a church group of some sort. I'm not sure, but they did have a few of the telltale signs, such as those little simplistic fish design lapel badges, extreme naïveté and a tendency to smile too pleasantly at each other. I felt tempted to explain to them how queuing worked, and suggest that it was all laid out fully in Helvetica, chapter six, if they needed to brush up on it, after three of them barged in front of me and stole the last of the sausages. There was the usual coach load of elderly tourists, possibly German, the men with their pastel Pringle-style sweaters tied around their necks and the women wearing Gary Larson cartoon spectacles and dripping in gold trinkets. There were also a few businessmen in suits, holding intense, humourless meetings over their croissants before they presumably scurried off to attend their awful I.T. trade shows in order to ogle the pneumatic promotion girls as they paraded up and down the aisles. I wondered if poor old Herr Fuchs had intended to meet up with someone over breakfast, to sell him a scissor-lift. Was he married, and did he have little children waiting for him back in Deutschland? The answers were just too painful to contemplate, and in a way, and quite a big way, his demise was my fault. If I hadn't been so damned stupid, he'd still be alive now. Had I not wearily accepted that smoking room, it would almost certainly have been me with my throat cut, and he'd have made his sales targets for another month and been awarded the engraved golf putter.

I made myself a cup of what passed for tea from the urn, found a quiet booth in the corner and slumped down into a window seat. I needed to think clearly about what I should do. It was now my responsibility to find the people who had done this to an innocent man before they had chance to do it to anyone else. As the tea kicked in, so the fog in my brain cleared. It was now obvious that the policemen back in England were phoney, and that, in turn, meant that all that bollocks about how they'd selected me for the mission was, well, bollocks. Having ascertained that there *was* no police intelligence – no computerized lists of people travelling to the Far East at their disposal, there was only one way these rat-bags could have known about my trip to Singapore, and that was Tina's Travel. It was only a matter of a few hours after my visit to the shop that the so-called boys in blue came a-calling, which meant one of two things. Either Tina was in on it, which was highly unlikely, or else someone had overheard my travel plans.

Then it hit me like a bolt from the blue. It must have been Inspector Clouseau. Not the real one, of course (if indeed there is a real one), but the shady character in the mac who kept turning up to browse through the travel brochures and never actually booking a holiday. Tina and I had suspected that he may be a pervert who got off by studying women in bikinis, but the truth was possibly even more sinister. He was the inside man that eavesdropped on the customers, waiting for those that were travelling to Singapore, or wherever his cronies needed their drugs to be smuggled to. No wonder I was paid in cash. A cheque would have revealed the true identity of the 'police officer'. And what a clever plan, in spite of Fu Manchu's offhand comment about the couriers being gullible. Mind you, I would say that, I suppose, to save face. It's just that, when two blokes come to your house in police uniforms, you naturally believe them to be policemen, don't you? I bet you would have done too, had you been in my shoes. I made a mental note to sneak into Fu Manchu's bedroom at police headquarters before I left, and superglue two black shoelaces under his nose in retaliation for the slight on my I.Q.

I took my mobile out of my shirt pocket and dialled Tina's Travel, but it was just the answering machine, so I asked if she could ring me as soon as was humanly possible. I even left my number to facilitate this, which I usually forget to do. Then I rang my parents' house to see how everything was going, and how Len was. My mother answered, and thanked me profusely for waking her up at two in the morning. I should have realized, but I'm hopeless with all that so many hours in front, so many hours behind, our winter is their summer thing. I was the same at school, when we had to try to answer those horrible maths questions about Jim digging a hole three yards wide by four yards long by two feet deep. They always needed to know how long it had taken him to dig it, and how much water it would hold, and frankly, I would glaze over at that point. I just didn't have that kind of a mind. In my defence, I was brilliant at the bit where we had to write an essay of a subject of our choice. All the others would scratch their heads and keep asking for clues on what to write about, but not me. The hardest part was getting me to stop. Anyway, I apologized to mother and volunteered to ring back at a more sociable hour, but she said that she was awake anyway, as some cretin had rung her in the middle of the night, so she might as well have a quick chat. I don't know where she gets that sarcastic streak from. Not from me, I'm sure. She informed me that Len was contented, had made my dad's favourite armchair his own, and had put on a couple of stone. Then she added something that made the invisible orchestra in the breakfast room strike up with those three power chords oft employed in made-for-TV suspense thrillers when something dramatic happens. She had taken Len for his teatime constitutional, and been given the honour of cleaning up after him.

'And do you know,' she added, 'that your dog is gifted? He can spell with his arse. He did eight dollops, which I thought was a bit excessive for a dog, and they looked like letters.'

I clutched my teacup for support. 'What did they spell, mom?' I asked breathlessly.

'Well, you won't believe this, our Adam,' she continued, 'but it looked just like NZ – created with six sort of sausage-shaped links – and then there was a perfect exclamation mark. He must have been really straining at the end, because he could only manage a little tiny plop, but it made the perfect full-stop shape!'

I thanked her profusely for her keen attention to detail, though it was just a tad too graphic for that time of the morning, if I'm honest, and especially just before a sortie to the hot counter, where a fresh load of sausages had just arrived. I told her I'd catch up when I was in New Zealand, and would remember the time difference next time. She grunted and put the phone down. I was going to call my ex and the kids next, but having been made aware of my timing error, I elected to do so later on. My mother could be fairly grumpy when awoken at ungodly hours, but compared to her ex-daughter-in-law she was sweetness and light personified. Had I stirred *her* from her slumbers in similar premature fashion, I would have risked having my eyeballs gouged out with her stick-on nails. Had I not been present in physical form to take my punishment, then my ears would have been subjected to so many unprintable curses that they would surely have wilted and died.

I helped myself to breakfast whilst grappling with Len's scatological warning. New Zealand's initials with an exclamation mark was nothing short of uncanny. I was actually beginning to suspect that he *was* really psychic after all. Stranger things have happened, you know. Look at that man who can recall facts about virtually anything he's ever read – the one that the film Rain Man was based on. And what about Stephen Wiltshire, the young black lad who can memorize entire cites and then draw them afterwards with perfect recall. There was another bloke on a TV documentary I saw, who could memorize an entire pack of cards in twenty-four seconds and replicate them. Autistic Savants, they're called. Awkward in company, in many ways socially inept, but always with a remarkable talent that can't be explained easily. 'There are more things in heaven and earth than are dreamt of in your philosophy', was how Shakespeare put it, but I reckon my mother summed it up even better. Len is a precociously gifted Autistic Savant dog who can, in her words, 'write with his arse'. When I got home, I resolved to study him more closely, and even loan him out to Oxford University for tests. Previously, I had imagined all he was doing when he got his nose stuck inside the dry food bag was trying to scoff the stuff. Now I suspect that he may well have been counting the pieces to keep his mind active, or maybe even calculating how many dinners he could get out of one full bag, based on an estimate of seventy per portion.

I decided to put this away for the time being, and instead, I turned my thoughts to organizing my day. Strangely, I was feeling remarkably light of spirit, considering the traumas I had suffered – the untimely death of Herr Fuchs, Len's warning, and the threat of assassination still potentially hanging over me. I put it down to the fact that I had slept well for a change, with no disconcerting dreams and no handcuffs to cut off my circulation. Even the sight of poor Herr Fuchs didn't instigate a nightmare. I'd been too exhausted to even dream, by the looks of things.

My plane left that evening at ten-thirty, so I had until teatime to explore. I wanted to see Raffles Hotel and the Chinese Quarter in particular, but I'd heard the chairlift over to the island was worth a trip and so was the zoo. I would have a day to spend in Singapore on the return journey too, so I could always squeeze in the things I had missed then, and it would have been crazy to simply dash around trying to fit it all in and not seeing anything properly. After much thought, I chose the Chinese Quarter first, so that I could fetch up at Raffles around five and experience one of their legendary afternoon teas.

I quickly completed my ablutions back at the hotel room and darted into the lift, lugging my bags behind me and avoiding all eye contact. I handed my luggage to the concierge, who locked it away safely and gave me a ticket. A policeman stood nearby in the lobby, keeping an eye on things after the incident the day before. He gave me a discreet wave as I strolled by, which was reassuring. As far as I was aware, whoever had come looking for me and the heroin didn't know what I looked like; they only knew my old room number, and this made me feel a lot better about tazzing around town with my Nikon digital camera, doing the tourist thing. They might have even been convinced that Herr Fuchs was indeed their man, and that he'd double-crossed them and fenced the goods, for which he'd paid the ultimate price. As far as they were concerned, it was job done and onto the next one. I sincerely hoped so.

I hailed a cab, asked for the Chinese Quarter, and ten minutes or so later I was dropped off at the Buddhist temple, which was next to the rabbit warren of alleyways to which I alluded earlier. The temple was very impressive, its rooftops adorned with life-sized multicoloured carvings of people and animals. Outside, scrawny men lounged around in their peculiar little pedal rickshaws, smoking, chatting, and waiting for the next punter to arrive. I took a sneaky picture of one of them, and then darted into the nearest alley. As I passed a photographic emporium, the diminutive salesman shot out and blocked my progress.

'What kind of camera do you have?' he asked.

'Oh, erm, a Nikon D40,' I replied.

'Very nice, very nice!' he remarked. 'Do you have a wide-anger rens for that?'

That wasn't a typographical error, by the way, though I daresay this thrilling account of my adventures does contain them. He pronounced 'lens' as 'rens'. Maybe he was Japanese, because I know the Chinese don't tend to do that 'L' and 'R' thing. I'd hate anyone to think that I was giving oriental people silly speech impediments just for comic effect.

Anyway, I digress. 'No, I don't,' I replied. Well, if there were three words that I've uttered in my life that I could have changed, it would have been those three. I would have substituted them for 'Yes I have.' It would have saved me countless hours of grief and stress, I can tell you. He invited me into the shop to take a look at his renses. I explained that I was not in the market for a new rens, but he insisted that this did not matter. He was merely showing me what could be achieved, photographically speaking, by employing the latest wide-angle technology, just for fun. I followed meekly, chuntering to myself about what a push-over I was. He slid open a glass cabinet window and produced a rens. He removed mine, without permission, and clicked his in place.

'A Nikon rens cost you prenty money, but this has same specification, same quarity at half the price. Rook, with your rens, you see half of shop. With mine – entire shop. How much are you wirring to pay?'

I reiterated that I was not looking to buy a wide-angle rens, at that precise moment in time. He produced a pocket calculator and tapped away at it furiously.

'My price for this rens, today onry, two hundred Engrish pounds.'

'I don't have two hundred *Engrish* pounds,' I replied, 'and if I did, I couldn't afford to spend it on a *rens*.'

'No, I didn't ask you to pay that much!' he explained, ignoring the fact that he had clearly done just that. 'That is my price for rens today, *usuarry*, but if you rike it, I can do this rens for (bashes away at calculator) just one hundred pounds.'

'It is a very good lens,' I said, 'but I don't want one. Or should I say, I'd like one, and it would be useful, I admit, but I don't have the spare money to throw around.'

'I can throw in a carrying case for your Nikon.'

'I've got one.'

'Frash gun.'

'No, thank you.'

'Trade is very poor this week. I have to make a sale.'

'Sorry to hear it, but not strictly my fault.'

'Rens and frash gun, forty pounds.'

'Look, I've only just got here. If every shop keeper accosts and kidnaps me I'll never get down to the end of this alley, and there are seventeen more alleys to go. I'll go away and think about it.'

'Thirty pounds.'

'No!'

(Taps calculator) 'Okay, twenty, and free Ervis DVD.'

'Oh, an Elvis DVD, well now you're talking!'

'So it's a deal?'

'No. That was sarcasm. Let me explain how it works. Usually, you just say the opposite of what you really mean, and the recipient usually gets it straight away.'

'Okay, I give you rens free.'

'I'll take it then.'

'You never heard of sarcasm, mister. Come on, ten pounds. I need a sale.'

And this is how it went on. I could not shake him. Not even when I curtly asked him to fuck off did it dampen his spirits. In the end, I just walked out with my fingers in my ears, humming a sea shanty. I rejoined the milling throng and continued down the alley. I'd gone all of four yards when I heard:

'What kind of camera is it, Mister?'

I cocked a deaf 'un and barged my way past. Already, I was hating this. Then I fell prey to the rabid pack of bespoke tailors. One bloke promised to make me a silk suit for a hundred quid and have it ready by that evening. Another wanted to sell me a batik dress for my wife for eighty-five pounds, which soon reduced to a more realistic seven pounds forty-nine. He virtually hung from my shorts, begging me, and in the end I had to flick him off and stride over his broken body in the gutter. I would love to have explained to them all that the English hate to be pestered whilst shopping. I've only got to hear an assistant back home ask, 'do you need any help?' and I'm out of there sharpish. Surely, someone from the Singapore tourist board should have a word, and ask the shop keepers to stand back and allow uninterrupted browsing. Then they would see their profits go sky-high, I'm sure. Somehow though, I fear they would not listen. This needless harassment is ingrained in their culture, just as being reserved is with the English. In the space of one hour, I had been accosted by no less than six 'won't hear the word no' camera shop assistants, and twice that many tailors. In the end, I just couldn't take any more, so I headed off to Raffles. It seemed a strange paradox that Singapore's taxi drivers were the least money-grabbing and pushy in the world, and yet its traders were the complete opposite. I vowed never to moan at English shop assistants again.

Raffles is impressive. It's a huge, white, colonial-style hotel with a maharajah-type bloke on the door, waiting to welcome you in. There are several floors, some private for the posh millionaire guests, so they don't have to mix with the riff-raff, and others boasting exclusive shops and boutiques that no one except the posh millionaires can afford to shop in anyway. Within the hotel are open quadrangles with exotic palm trees and flowering shrubs, fountains and covered walkways with ceiling fans everywhere in case it's a bit hot, which it usually is. In the Long Bar, the afternoon drinkers sip their Singapore slings, just as Noel Coward and Ernest Hemingway did all those years ago. There are barrels of peanuts to encourage the drinkers to drink more, and tradition dictates that the shells are thrown onto the bar-room floor so that, by the end of the evening, you're waist deep in them. I didn't sample a Singapore sling, however, because I tend not to drink alcohol mid-afternoon. I'm strictly a tea man until the sun has gone over the yard arm (whatever that is), and after that I hit the red like it's about to go out of fashion. Consequently, I gave the Long Bar a miss and headed for the Tiffin Room to sample its legendary afternoon tea. I was directed to a seat by another maharajah-type and handed a menu, and then my mobile rang. It was Tina, answering my earlier call. I explained to her the predicament I found myself in, going into great detail, being as she was paying for the call. She was aghast, to put it mildly. Apparently, old Inspector Clouseau had been in again recently, hung around for ages and walked out without a word, so it was feasible, she agreed, if a little far-fetched, that he could have been touting for potential drug smugglers. I asked her to do me a great favour and contact the police – preferably some real ones – and explain what had happened to me. I felt sure that if they cased her joint and lay in wait for this man, he could be leant on. If my theory was correct and he was in cahoots with the two who visited me, then maybe an entire drug-smuggling gang could be bought to book before anyone else had their windpipe exposed. Then I had a brainwave. Fu Manchu had asked for the hotel's CCTV tapes, which reminded me that there might have been footage in existence of my two pretend coppers, back in England. I gave her the dates and fairly precise timings, and I could hear her diligently scribbling it down on her jotting pad. She promised to do her best and put the phone down before the call wiped out her entire year's profits. It was just after she had gone that I remembered how mobiles worked, and I blanched beneath my tan. A friend of mine had recently been on holiday in Spain, when he received a business call from someone in Bulgaria that went on and on. It was only when he got his bill that he realized that he had subsidized the call to the tune of thirty-five quid. That said, if my prolonged chat with Tina resulted in the arrest of five ruthless criminals, it was worth every penny.

The maharajah, who had gone into hibernation inside his turban whilst I rattled on, spotted that I had at last finished my business and approached once more, bringing over one of those tiered cake stand affairs and a silver teapot. He poured me a cup, and then asked what I wanted from the menu. I explained that I didn't want anything, as the contents of his cake stand would have fed a double-decker bus full of pensioners for a fortnight. He gave a haughty sniff and sidled off, but not before he'd handed me the bill, hidden in a posh leather-bound wallet. I nearly choked on my smoked salmon and cream cheese blini. All I wanted was a few cups of tea, a sandwich or three and a bit of cake. I didn't realize that they expected me to pay their mortgage that month. Jeez! By my reckoning, there were sixteen fancy cakes, thirty assorted sandwiches and a dozen scones with jam and cream for one person. Then he was trying to get me to sign up for chicken and rice from the hot section, and Lord knows what else besides. Who did he think I was? Billy Bunter? The contents of his cake stand alone would have put me in the seriously obese category. Given the amount I was likely to eat, every little tiny cake would have cost as much as a Cessna four-seater aeroplane, plus a year's hangar fees. I called him over for a discreet word. Ten seconds later, I was turfed out and back on the street, feeling ever so slightly foolish, having reluctantly parted with twenty-five quid in order to avoid a night in a tough Singapore jail full of addicts, psychopaths and paedophiles. Either that or dishwashing duties, which is even worse. I'm so squeamish about touching anyone else's dinner plates!

I decided to catch a cab back to my hotel and doze in one of the foyer's armchairs until the transfer bus arrived to take me to Changi airport. All of a sudden it was dawning on me that there was a hell of a way to travel before I reached New Zealand, and just the thought of it was making me feel completely shattered. After five minutes, my taxi driver pulled up, but we weren't at Clarke Quay or anywhere I recognized, so I asked him why we'd stopped.

'What time your plane leave?' he enquired.

'Half-past ten tonight,' I replied, puzzled.

'Plenty time!' he grinned. 'This is Sim Lim Square. Very good electrical goods. My cousin, Bert Chang, have nice shop here, floor number five. Very reasonable. You have very nice Nikon camera. He sell you wide-angle lens, very cheap. Hundred English pounds. In England, it cost you loads more. I wait here, you go see my cousin. He do you good deal.'

I dragged myself wearily out of the cab and made for the front steps. Sometimes it is just easier to just bite the bullet and buy the God-damned rens. I tried to convince myself that it would come in handy for all those legendary New Zealand panoramas.

Top 10 HOLIDAY PARKS

CHIPTAH 9

In which I familiarize myself with the Kore-Take.

The first picture I took with my 'wide-anger rens' when I got to New Zealand was of the back of the giant 747 that had been my home for ten hours since I'd departed from Changi Airport, and boy, was I glad to see the back of that plane. I have to grudgingly admit that it was a very useful lens, and twenty quid was a bargain, though I would have secretly preferred the logo on the side to have said Nikon, and not Sakakaki – whoever they are.

The journey had been tough. The previous flight was just about tolerable, largely due to the fact that outside it was daylight most of the time and I could read, watch a film, ogle the lovely Geisha or eat. The Singapore to New Zealand leg began at around the time that sensible folks went to bed, so once the formalities and safety procedures were dealt with, most of the passengers rolled over and started snoring profusely, to the point where I genuinely believed I was not in an aeroplane at all, but in a huge, uncomfortable flying pigsty. Unable to sleep a wink, I followed the plane's progress by watching the computerized map of the earth on the little TV screen in front of me. The red line showed our flight path, and man, it was slow. Eventually, after what seemed like months spent in captivity, there was a little buzz of excitement amongst the passengers as we reached the tip of Australia. 'Nearly there now!' I convinced myself, but my oh my, was I ever wrong. Five hours later, we were still passing over it, and all I could see below were vast swathes of nothingness, broken only by single, dead-straight tracks for hundreds of miles that seemed to lead to just one house. It reminded me of an excellent joke I once heard about a cowboy, alone on the prairie, mending his fences. Suddenly, a voice behind him speaks and puts the fear of God into him. The owner of the voice introduces himself as the cowboy's 'next-door neighbour', from the Big G Ranch, some twenty miles away.

'Sorry to scare yer, partner,' says the powerfully built stranger, removing his Stetson and wiping the sweat from his brow. 'There's a party tomorrow night at the Big G. There's gonna be barbecued steaks, a few barrels of good beer, some fancy dancin', followed by a whole lot of hot sex and, who knows? Even a few fist fights. Wondered if you'd care to come.'

'Sure thing!' smiled the cowboy. 'Glad to oblige. What do I wear?'

'Hell, it don't matter none,' explained the stranger, 'On account of it's only gonna be you and me!'

Australia did eventually, after much begging and pleading on my part, recede into the distance, and an hour or two later the captain finally announced that we were about to land. I don't mind admitting that I felt quite emotional at that point, and even more so when the doors finally opened and we shuffled out into a pleasant, English-style summer's day.

New Zealand's customs officers, much to my surprise, were humourless, American-style characters, and far stricter than their European counterparts. I understand that they are only trying to keep their beloved country free of imported diseases, but I had the feeling that, had I accidentally sneaked in a cubic millimetre of corned beef, trapped in my turn-up, I'd have been taken out the back, tortured and shot. I dropped my backpack onto the conveyor, took a fortifying gulp, and waited to see what, if anything, happened. Something did. The X-ray operative asked me to open the bag and remove the contents. I took out Mr Maori and showed it to him with trembling hand. He called his colleague over to take

110

a look, and he, in turn called two more. They picked the carving up, stared at it, shook it and put it down again. Then one of them asked me a question.

'G'day!' he began, which I thought was more of an Australian greeting. I reciprocated with a friendly nod. 'Hiv you iver heard of the ixprission, 'Taking coals to Newcastle?'' he asked, without cracking his face.

'Yes, of course,' I replied.

'Fair enough,' he conceded, his face registering puzzlement. Hiv a nice day!'

And with that, I was allowed to progress to the baggage reclaim.

A short while later, I emerged, dazed and confused from Christchurch airport into the warm sunshine, pushing my intoxicated trolley before me. I was so zombified now that I could have easily landed a bit-part in *Shaun of the Dead*, and the director would have been able to spot my potential even without make-up. I was desperate for a good sleep again, but I still had to travel a mile by courtesy bus to pick up my Kore-Take motor home. True to form, one had just departed, which meant I had another half an hour to wait. I needed to phone Katie and the kids, but I had no idea whatsoever what the time was back in England. I'd just about got used to Singapore being eight hours behind – or was it in front? – and now I had to start all over again. I sat on the pavement with my back against the luggage trolley and closed my eyes. A few seconds later, I felt someone prodding me on the shoulder. I groggily forced my eyes open. Looking down at me and blotting out most of the light was a huge Maori-looking individual with a massive grin on his face. It was my bus driver, and I'd been asleep for half an hour. Either that or he was seriously early.

'Vin hire?' he asked.

'Vin?' I queried, puzzled.

'Kimper vin,' he explained, or rather, he thought he had.

'Sorry?' I frowned. I was, in my defence, still half asleep.

'Motor home?'

Now I understood. These people really did mangle their vowels – the reports I'd heard were no exaggeration. I stood up wearily and the man mountain kindly threw my heavy bag on board as if it were a packet of Ryvita. I quickly grabbed the backpack to prevent Mr Maori from being turned into matchwood and followed the driver onto the bus. I was the only passenger. Ten minutes later, the vehicle came to a halt, the doors hissed open and I jumped off with my stuff. Mr Maori – the human one, not the carving – wished me a cheery 'G'day!' and pulled away.

So far, New Zealand looked like any other trading estate, and I was a bit disappointed. I'd travelled thousands of miles over often inhospitable countries – places that were totally alien to my way of life and culture – and all of a sudden I was back in familiar territory. It could easily have been West Bromwich. Of course, I was sensible enough to realize that everywhere has its trading estates and industrial areas so I didn't let this spoil things, but I'd rather hoped that my first view of such a special place could have been majestic snow-capped mountains and maybe a mirror lake, just to get me in the mood. Instead, I was staring at the NZ equivalent of a Kwik Fit factory, a McDonalds, a large discount tile warehouse and a forecourt full of Kore-Take motor homes. I lugged my baggage over to the front doors and struggled in.

I like descriptive writing as much as the next man, but there is a time and place for it, and a time when it is not called for. Waxing lyrical about the sixty-seven forms I had to fill in, the photocopies that had to be made of birth certificates, insurance documents, health forms, driving licence and all my old 'O' level and 'A' level certificates as well, doesn't strike me as riveting from a reader's point of view, so I've merely given you a flavour and I'll let you imagine the rest. Suffice it to say that, by the time I was sat at the wheel of my Kore-Take Explorer Four Berth and ready to pull away, after my brief two-hour guided tour, safety talk and operational run-through, I was more than ready to get up again, slump into the nearest of those four berths and give up for the day. Camping out for the night in front of the hire company's offices was not an option for several reasons, however, so with more than a little trepidation, I kangarooed off the forecourt and turned left as instructed by Asif, my Indian instructor, who looked like a twelve-year-old with a moustache. Quite what I was supposed to do next wasn't clear, but I didn't want to pull up and study my map until they couldn't see me any more – otherwise I'd have looked like the completely clueless, incompetent, geographically dyslexic Pom that I was.

Asif had explained that there were hundreds of caravan sites all over the country, and the ones owned by a company called Top Ten were pretty good (or Top Tin as he pronounced it). They were depicted as little blue camper van logos on the extortionately expensive map he had sold me, and there were also variations on this symbol, showing the same blue van, but with what I took to be shit coming from beneath it into some form of bucket. These indicated camps with dump sites, for emptying the chemical toilet. I was far too exhausted to drive far, so I pinpointed a site that looked close by, and aimed for that. To say that I was nervous would be an understatement. At home, I'd been used to driving what amounted to a large pram with an engine in it, and now here I was in an alien environment, trying to tackle a small house on wheels. I arrived at the Te-Anachokkibikki campsite (or whatever it was bloody called) some thirty minutes later, soaked in sweat and completely wired, like I was a crack cocaine addict or something. I was aware that this place wasn't one of Top Ten's places, but I was far too knackered to care.

I coughed up my thirty dollars to the fat lady in the nylon dressing gown and made my way to pitch number forty-seven, which was conveniently next to the shower block. I hooked up the electricity cable as instructed, and decided to have a quick look in the fridge to see if old Asif had left me a welcome pack. 'As if!' I quipped as I did so, rather wittily I thought. I was desperate for a cup of tea, and a round of toast would have been nice. What I didn't expect was the fridge door falling off when I opened it. A couple of little bars and screws had worked their way loose, and rolled down the steps to the van's side door, which was, of course, open at the time. I spent the next fifteen minutes trying to find them in the undergrowth, and a further fifteen fathoming out how they went together again and held the door on. Meanwhile, inside the fridge, things weren't any better. Asif was no doubt aware that it was his duty to provide the welcome pack, but ultimately decided that he couldn't be arsed to fetch one, and consequently, just like Old Mother Hubbard's fridge, mine was bare, if one excluded the cryogenically preserved woodlouse.

Luckily, the site boasted a shop, if a shelf containing one box of PG tips, a sausage roll, two Kit Kats, several cartons of long-life milk, an assortment of fishing lines, a cereal bar of dubious vintage and a box of Kellogg's Cornflakes constituted a shop. I purchased the cornflakes, the long-life milk and the teabags, reducing the contents of the shelf by almost half, and strolled back to the van, pondering as to whether 'long-life' referred to the milk's sell-by-date or the purchaser's health after drinking the stuff. Judging by the effect it had on the taste of my tea, 'short-life' would have been more accurate, if the latter were the case. I ate half the box of cornflakes and watched with a mixture of fascination and horror as my stomach swelled up to the size of a hot-air balloon. It was late afternoon now and I was starving and tired in equal measure. I knew that if I dozed off, I'd end up with my body completely out of sync, so I decided to take a shower using the tokens I had been given at reception, in the hope that it would revitalize me until bedtime. Then I intended to explore the locality in search of a good pizza restaurant.

I strode over to the breeze-block shower facility whistling a jaunty tune, as is traditional, with my towel, soap and shampoo under my arm. This was the life, I convinced myself. It reminded me of all the camping holidays I had been on with my mom and dad, and I admit that I became a little sentimental. I was twelve thousand miles from home, but I could have been in Tenbury Wells, Worcestershire, or maybe Bridgnorth; it felt so familiar. I expected to see a row of beer-bellied middle-aged men in white vests, shaving themselves and whistling furiously, but I had the place to myself. I suppose, with a population of just four and a half million, this was going to be the case a lot of the time. I located the showers, a block of three cubicles, and took my pick. Inside each one there was a sort of tiny ante-room with a few coat hangers and a wooden slatted seat. Past this was the shower cubicle itself, separated from the miniscule changing area by a white shower curtain which had turned a fetching shade of green from the bottom quarter down. I slipped off my stale, sweaty clothing, pushed the token into the machine and was heartened to observe the shower head springing to life and producing lovely, steaming hot water. The tokens lasted six minutes, according to Nylon Nora, so I didn't waste any time getting in there, and I have to report that, whilst it would struggle to command a feature in 'Homes and Gardens', it was nevertheless warm and workmanlike and I was extremely grateful. True to form, the water ran out after what seemed to be two, rather than six minutes, but I put that down to my losing track of time due to the pleasantness of it all. Covered in soap, which was now stinging my eyes badly, I staggered out and retrieved the other token from my shorts, noticing that I had omitted to lock the outer door. Unperturbed, due to the singular lack of campers, I quickly slotted the token into the machine and shot back under the shower head to wash my hair and rinse away all the lather before I ran out of credit.

Suddenly, the shower curtain was wrenched back to reveal a massive Maori man, plastered in tattoos and stark naked except for his sunglasses. Had I been suffering with constipation, this terrifying vision would have served me far better than Ex-Lax.

'Where is it?' he snarled, his huge right hand reaching for my throat.

I cowered against the cold, cracked tiles of the cubicle, quaking with fear. 'Where's what?' I implored. 'What do you want?'

'Where is it?' he repeated menacingly. It was like that scene in *Marathon Man*, when Laurence Olivier keeps repeating, 'Is it safe?' and poor old Dustin Hoffman hasn't got a clue what he's on about. The giant right hand tried to tear my throat out then, but I ducked, showing a rare burst of agility brought about by a desire to see my next birthday. Spotting daylight in the gap under his lunging right arm and his gigantic black body, I lurched forward, and somehow managed to slide between the two, largely thanks to being lubricated by the liberal layer of lather still clinging to my weedy white body. Thinking quickly, I decided against hanging around in the tiny ante-room to neatly fold my clothes and towel, and instead rocketed out of the cubicle like a whippet, heading for the comparative safety of my motor home. As I belted out of the shower block, covered in foam and as naked as the day I was born, I collided with an elderly gentleman who was just arriving to perform his ablutions, and laid him on his back. Usually I am the very soul of good manners and politeness, but I confess that I continued on my way without as much as a backwards glance. It was the same when, seconds later, I sprinted past Nylon Nora, who was just heading over to the laundry with a basket of clothes. I felt sure I'd eventually have a lot of explaining to do, if the good Lord spared my life to tell the tale.

I bounded up to the motor home, wrenched open the side door and leapt inside, pulling the door shut behind me and frantically searching, alas, in vain, for bolts to slide across. I closed all the Draylon curtains, quickly dried myself as best I could with the dishcloth, and pulled on some clothing from my case. Then, breathlessly, I peeked at the entrance to the shower block through a small gap in the curtains for signs of the man mountain. Somehow, this hell-hound had been tracking me, intent on retrieving the blasted evil white powder for his masters, and judging by his opening gambit, he didn't seem overly fussed if he disembowelled me in the process.

116

After five minutes of vigilance, I observed him leaving the building, as casual as you like, glancing menacingly this way and that before thankfully heading off in the opposite direction. Now I was in deep trouble. These people seemed to have agents everywhere, and even in New Zealand, I wasn't safe. I decided to run over to Nylon Nora's reception area under cover of darkness and demand that she phoned for some police protection, pronto.

A sudden loud knock on my door saw my heart shoot out of my mouth and catapult around the motor home before returning to its cage. I pulled open the kitchenette drawers and found a potato peeler. It wasn't great, but it would have to do. I'd rather hoped to stab him in the chest, not gently peel him while we sat chatting on the settee, but beggars can't be choosers. The Kore-Take was so basic, Jamie Oliver would have struggled to create a cheese sandwich with lettuce. I tip-toed over to the side window and lifted the curtain an inch. It was Nora. I nervously opened the door and asked her to come in, and sharpish.

She obliged, but warned me that, if there was any funny business, she had a personal alarm. I assured her that I was not the lunatic that I appeared, and explained that there was a perfectly rational reason for my nude one hundred metres record attempt. This seemed to pacify her enough to venture inside and take a seat. I think she was also heartened by the fact that I was now dressed and decent again.

'I need you to call the cops right away,' I pleaded. 'There are some people following my every move – they have been since England, and I'm frightened for my life. Just now, I was having a shower, and this huge, naked bloke burst in and tried to strangle me.'

'I know,' she replied.

'You do?' I asked.

'Yis. He's just told me.'

'Well, we need to inform the police,' I insisted. 'The man's highly dangerous.'

'No, he's not,' said Nora. 'What you've told me about being followed might or might not be true, but that bloke you jist bumped into is harmless. He's also blind and dif.'

'What?'

'Blind and dif. I just talked to Myra, his wife. He just told her that somebody just frightened the life out of him in the showers. Apparently, he felt his way into what he thought was an unoccupied cubicle, slipped his shorts down and pulled back the curtain. He didn't realize you were in there because he didn't hear the water running and he couldn't see you.'

'Shit!' I sighed. 'But hang on, why was he saying, 'where is it?' and trying to strangle me then?'

Nora gave a hearty laugh that sounded like a hyena choking on a chunk of road-kill possum.

'He was ifter the soap, thit's all. He knows we always leave a bar in there, but the bugger can nivva find it, and gits mad with himsilf. You pushing past him just now gave him the fright of his life, I can tell you. Nixt time, I suggist you remember to lock the bladdy door, mate – and I bit he used up your token as well, just to teach you a lisson!'

Well, have you ever felt a complete fool? I'd been at the site less than ten minutes, and already I'd had an altercation in the showers with a giant disabled Maori and streaked naked past the receptionist. Thank God my todger had been more or less covered by a strategically placed dollop of foam. What could I do for an encore, I wondered. Somehow, I didn't think it would be too long before I provided the answer to that.

118

CHIPTAH 10

*In which I embark on the first leg of my NZ adventure, and
discover multiple uses for a possum.*

I awoke with a glorious bar of white sunlight branding my chest,
to the sound of birds twittering, and for the first time since leaving
England I felt a lightness of spirit, coupled with the dawning
realization that I was beginning a new and exciting 'chiptah' of
my life. The farcical shower episode just seemed to highlight the
fact that I was finally free of drug-smuggling assassins and I could
now concentrate on enjoying my holiday. I folded away the bed
and set up the breakfast table as Asif had instructed me. After
much thought, I decided upon cornflakes and a cup of tea for
breakfast. It would have to suffice until I could get underway, and
maybe visit a supermarket. I was extremely eager to explore
Christchurch before I set off, as I had heard it was a very English-
looking city, so I wolfed down my meagre repast and was about to
head for the shower block to use the lavatory and brush my teeth,
when I realized that I had my own shower, lavatory and wash
basin on board. Asif had suggested I use the shower only when
unavoidable because it used up precious water, and likewise the
chemical lavatory, because I'd have to empty it regularly, which
wasn't pleasant. Ideally, these on-board facilities were only
intended for emergency use, when marooned between sites, so I
slipped on my clothes and was just about to head across to the
showers, when I saw the blind, deaf Maori doing likewise, guided
this time by his wife, Myra, who was holding a mop, presumably

121

for protection. Not really wishing to meet up with him again for reasons of embarrassment, I reluctantly decided that I'd use my own lavatory. After all, I had no chance of keeping it in pristine condition for an entire month, and I wasn't scared of a bit of mucking out when the time came. I'd produced two children and regularly changed their nappies when they were small, so after that, a chemical toilet held no fear. I sat myself down and studied my expensive map as I emptied myself, trying to plot my best route into town. I was feeling far better now that I'd slept, and a healthy bowel movement was, I felt, the icing on the cake. I was feeling full of the joys of spring; even though I felt sure it was actually late summer Down Under.

I laid down my map and reached for the flusher, and that's where it all went wrong. Without warning, the shower came on, soaking me from head to foot and ruining my expensive map. I must admit that I screamed, which, on reflection, was rather a girly thing to do. I quickly shoved the lever back into position, and then I noticed the toilet flush – a small button situated on the cistern. I squelched out of the tiny white plastic broom closet and set about organizing a change of clothing.

The previous evening had also not gone according to plan, though maybe I should have known it wouldn't. Not wishing to stray too far on my first night, I elected to take a stroll around the perimeter of the depressing trading estate where my campsite was situated, in search of pizza. They often say that New Zealand is a bit like England used to be thirty years ago, and this is true with regard to pizzas, if nothing else. Nowadays in the mother country, pizzas tend to fall into two distinct camps – the true Italian and the foul American. The former: light, thin and crispy with minimal toppings, plus of course oregano and proper mozzarella; the latter: two inches thick, full of fried fat and with sixty-four species of disgusting crap and a combination of cheddar and toenail cheese on top. The New Zealand pizza, however, fell into neither category. It resembled an inedible prototype, more than anything. It was as if antipodean food spies, having heard all about these mysterious round, continental specialities and wishing to clone them, had taken secret photographs of real pizzas using a telephoto rens, and then set about reconstructing the things back in their secret food laboratory. Consequently, from a distance, the New Zealand pizza appeared convincing, but as with all prototypes, they are not really intended to be used, or in this case, eaten.

The base, for example, was round, I'll grant you, which was, one might argue, a good start, but it was just *too* round. It appeared to have been created from MDF and cut out with a precision press. When cooked, it took on the characteristics of a very hard biscuit – a bit like the ones that my dog Len likes to chew on for up to three hours. Then there was the topping. Through his telephoto rens, the spy would have observed that the authentic pizza had some form of red smear on top of it, and this had faithfully been reproduced back in the lab, in terms of its pantone colour, at least. Having never got close enough to taste one, however, he would not have realized that it was tomato-based, rather than just created with red acrylic paint. In short, and some would argue that none of this diatribe could be described as short, New Zealand is at the very start of its learning curve vis-à-vis the pizza, and I'm sure that, when I return in another thirty or so years, they will no doubt boast a product that even retired folk from Napoli would approve of. Until then, I advise you, if you ever find yourself down that way, to buy a cheese and ham toastie instead. That said, it seemed silly to travel halfway around the globe in order to eat pizzas, so I decided to write off my first day, chalk it up to experience and look forward to my trip to Christchurch.

Christchurch was very nice. It was as if loads of ex-pats were pining for England, so they designed the place to look like an amalgam of Oxford and Cambridge. There was even a nice shallow river flanked by weeping willows running through it with men in Oxford blazers and straw boaters punting the tourists up and down. In a word, Idyllic. The only downside was that the tourist population was largely made up of Japanese, and whilst I have nothing against the Japanese – other than that their ancestors tortured my granny's next-door neighbour and beheaded several of his mates in front of his eyes for not showing due respect – I do find their habit of constantly photographing everything they come across on this planet very annoying. They take so many pictures that there surely can't be enough time left in their lives to actually look at them all. Being a tad more selective wouldn't do them any harm either. I know you'll accuse me of gross exaggeration, but I swear that the ones I observed in Christchurch took pictures of a McDonalds restaurant frontage, a random waste-paper bin, a non-descript sapling tree, and literally millions of shots of each other, grinning and pointing at everything that moved, or for that matter, didn't. One chap, sat outside a café waiting for his lunch, asked his girlfriend to photograph him with his table marker – those things that look like flags with your table number written on them, so that the waiter can find you. He sat there grinning like an idiot, just pointing at the number forty-six. I wouldn't have minded so much if he'd *been* forty-six, but he was about twenty-seven.

If you like street entertainment, Christchurch is your place, especially on a weekend. There were eight-year-old violinists all over the place, some playing quaint Japanese and Chinese music, others Irish jigs, classical or jazz. There were two lads of around twelve with electric guitars and little amplifiers, belting out a spirited if distorted version of *Sweet Home Alabama*. Just down the road, an old bloke was trying to persuade his pet dog to perform on a skateboard, and next to him, the inevitable pretend statue man was scaring the toddlers to death. Trolley buses, manned by folks in period costume clattered by, lone saxophonists with their obligatory ponytails serenaded the outdoor diners, and if none of that was up your street, you could always watch the Japs photographing the street signs, so they'd know where they'd been when they got home.

I wandered into a rather posh store, just nosing around, and after a while it was obvious to me that New Zealanders hated possums, or Opossums, to give them their seldom-used correct spelling. Everything seemed to be made from possum fur. You could get possum coats, possum cushions and possum possums (little toy possums made from real possum fur). There were T shirts with the slogan, 'Possums – Nature's Little Speed Bumps' which I thought a bit cruel being an animal lover myself, but one friendly shop assistant explained the reason for this. Apparently, these creatures are not indigenous to New Zealand, but were introduced by some cretin because he thought the place would look more cheerful with a few of them waddling around. The only problem was, the possums ate most of the Kiwis and much else besides, so the good people of the islands decided to flatten them at every opportunity and turn them into tourist goods.

I mentioned the friendly shop assistant just now. In London, coming across such a person would be worthy of comment, as most of them hate their customers with a vengeance. Not so in New Zealand. As far as I could make out, with my admittedly limited experience, everyone seemed willing to bend over backwards to help, even in such a big city. It could only get friendlier in the smaller towns I reckoned, and all in all, even though I didn't really wish to spend too much time in shopping centres, this was an encouraging start. I purchased a little possum made of possum, a little kiwi made from possum and a little tattooed Maori man with hair made from, you've guessed it, possum, and then headed back to the motor home, which I'd parked on the outskirts of town. I intended to play fighting games with them on the breakfast table if I got bored at any time. The little Maori came with a plastic spear, but I was going to lend the possum a potato peeler to make it fair. The kiwi had a long sharp beak, so he was okay.

I consulted my new expensive map. (My old expensive map was now no more than squidgy pulp, thanks to the impromptu shower.) The trick was to cover a fair bit of ground during daylight hours, stopping off here and there to look at things and eat, and aim for a site around teatime. I fancied taking a peek at Mount Cook, where old Edmund Hillary used to practise his climbing before he took on Everest, so I decided to set sail for Lake Tekapo, which was halfway there.

The suburbs of Christchurch looked quite well-to-do, with some impressive colonial houses. I became quite an expert at navigating these streets, once I'd been round them for the seventeenth time. At first, I just thought I was experiencing a sense of déjà-vu, but when I realized that I'd passed Papanui for the eighth time in fifteen minutes, I decided to get help. I asked an elderly lady how to get on the 77 motorway towards Timaru, and she informed me, with a dead straight face, that I was starting from the wrong place to get there. Eventually though, she gave me precise instructions, and ten minutes later, I was back in Papanui. I made a mental note to hack off the head of the Head of Town Planning with a Samurai sword, should our paths ever cross, and they probably would have done, thanks to the way they'd buggered up the road signs. It was then that I had a brainwave. I turned round and followed a sign for Papanui, and hey presto, I joined the 77 motorway heading for Timaru, seconds before I would have been tempted to end my sorry life with my potato peeler, in the absence of a service revolver.

It was a long drive, but there were so few cars on the road that it was an absolute pleasure, and the scenery was stunning. I reckon I only passed fourteen vehicles during a three-hour drive, but at least nine hundred 'bas relief' possums, and this set me thinking. In a country with so few people and cars, these possums must surely be the most unlucky creatures ever to have existed. I could have crossed a country road blindfolded and wearing earplugs at any time of the day or night and not encountered an oncoming lorry, just because the odds were stacked in my favour. As far as I could work out, the mathematical probability of colliding with anything was a million to one, but somehow, these nocturnal pests seemed to be virtual vehicle magnets, which meant one of two things. Either they were being deliberately stalked and aimed at for sport, or else they had bred with lemmings, and inherited a suicide gene. Perhaps it was one of those self-fulfilling prophecies.

126

The creatures had become seriously depressed, due to seeing their loved ones lying dead everywhere, and consequently resolved to end it all in the same fashion, thus adding to the general state of world weariness that possum psyche was heir to. If this *were* the case, they must be very patient creatures, because it would surely take an hour of standing around on the M77 before anything drove by to flatten them. Maybe they listened to Leonard Cohen albums on their little iPods while they waited, just to get them in the right mood. Either that or they read a Salman Rushdie novel.

I couldn't help thinking that these poor possums were the innocents in all this, and were paying a huge price, thanks entirely to the mindless turd who introduced them in the first place. Our children often complain that they didn't ask to be born – though when I then offer to end it all for them with a potato peeler they quickly capitulate. I wonder if the young possum mantra is, *I didn't ask to be introduced here*, when its parents ask it to tidy up its burrow.

I had already given far too much head-space to possums for one day, so I rerouted my train of thought to the magnificent views that I had experienced during my drive. A lot of people who travel to New Zealand will tell you that you get heartily sick of your travelling companion constantly asking you to 'look at that wonderful view', because you could potentially hear it every ten seconds, once you've cleared the inner-city trading estates. With that in mind, I would ask you to presume the view is nearly *always* stunning, unless I state otherwise, and if I am tempted to comment on a view it will be because it was exceptionally, mind-blowingly fantastic, as opposed to the rest of the bog-standard superlative stuff on offer.

As I left the city suburbs behind, I noticed that the dwellings became far more, shall we say, rustic. Houses were constructed of shiplap, usually painted white or rust red, with green corrugated metal roofs – a bit like posh English sheds or small village cricket pavilions. The nicer ones had a covered porch, and reminded me not of England thirty years ago, but small town America – the way

I presume New England looks, though I haven't actually been there. Everyone has those post-boxes on poles at the end of the garden, by the roadside, the way the Americans do, and everything was made of wood – even the churches. Christchurch *was* full of brick buildings and looked as English as chicken tikka, but every town I drove through now looked like those frontier towns you see in cowboy films. Shops either side of one long high street, covered walkways with rails where you can tie your horse, art deco pubs with names like The Golden Nugget Saloon and beaten up, dusty pick-up trucks. This was a gold rush country, after all, way back in the early nineteen hundreds, just as America was. To me, the resemblance was not what I expected, but sort of sentimental nevertheless. Eventually, I drove into Lake Tekapo, which was just gorgeous: the sun making the water twinkle with a million tiny starburst lights. I found the Top Tin, paid my forty dollars (I hoped it didn't get dearer by increments of ten dollars each day), parked up for the night, and set off in search of sustenance and a glass or two of red 'to help sleep me', as my mother would say.

The site was a few miles out of town, so I hopped on a bus and leapt off at what I hoped was the town centre. I spent a few minutes comparing restaurants and settled for one that had a nice log fire and a pool table. Once seated in the special area reserved for single people with no mates, I began to peruse the menu, and noticed that this place, like several others I'd seen, offered the curiously titled Blue Cod. There was plain Blue Cod, served with chips and salad, Blue Cod wrapped in a light beer batter, and a tourist special wrapped in possum fur. I chose the beer battered one, and I'm pleased to report that it was not only *not* blue, which was a blessing, but also very good. I now knew that if ever I were struggling with New Zealand cuisine, I could always fall back on the Blue Cod. I would survive by becoming Blue Cod Man, a bit like the gastronomic version of Blue Harbour Man at Marks and Spencers' – never too adventurous, but you're guaranteed to look okay in it, in that middle-aged, middle-class kind of way.

No sooner had I forked in the last morsel when my mobile rang, signalling another smash and grab raid on my bank account. Thankfully, while stocking up my wonky fridge at one of the many small convenience stores en route (curiously referred to as dairies), I enquired about the public telephones and was sold a little paper receipt with a printed number on it, which the proprietor assured me would save me money when phoning overseas. All I had to do was type in this number before I dialled, and money was deducted for each call I made until the fee was used up. I just hoped that I hadn't been duped, and charged twenty dollars for an old petrol receipt he'd found under the counter.

I answered my phone and implored the caller to keep it brief, even before I knew who was calling me. It was Tina, from Tina's Travel, reporting back with the latest developments. The police were interested in my strange tale, but couldn't really post a plain-clothed man in the shop for days on end in the vain hope of spotting Clouseau walk in. I had to admit that this was a fair point. Then I had a good idea. I asked Tina to pop next door to the bookshop where my mate Jake worked. Jake was a good-looking little Australian lad from the Blue Mountains of Sydney, who, for some obscure reason, had swapped one of the most beautiful places in the world for Stourbridge High Street. The weirdest thing is; he actually seems to prefer it. Either that or he can't scrape the airfare together to get back, and he's putting a brave face on it. Anyway, I asked Tina to visit Jake and explain the Clouseau scenario. Jake was game for just about anything, being Australian, and he even looked like he could be a great drug smuggler, so if Clouseau arrived, she could make a quick, cryptic call to Jake, and he'd march in from next door and loudly demand information on flights to Singapore, giving Tina details of his address and phone number through a megaphone, just to make sure Clouseau got them. Then, unless I was very much mistaken, the bogus boys in blue would contact my friend within the week, arrange a visit, and be ambushed by the real boys in blue – if they could be arsed to turn up after being guaranteed a collar without having to do much to earn it. Tina seemed genuinely thrilled to be part of such a daring adventure and promised to do her best. I added that, if Jake wasn't keen on getting involved, she should apply subtle psychological pressure by reminding him that he still owed me fifty quid for my old mountain bike – a debt that I would wipe from the records if he cooperated fully.

After wrapping things up with Tina, I played a few games of pool with a couple of friendly local lads, and I have to report that they were soundly thrashed, thanks to my misspent youth. The loser supplied the drinks and by half-nine the pool table appeared to be gently revolving. I decided to retire unbeaten at that point, before the table developed twelve pockets. I wished them goodnight and decided to try out my phone-card device before I caught the bus back to the site. Happily, it worked a treat, and I was able to catch up with Katie and the kids for a considerable time without having to plan a bullion heist in Auckland to help finance it. What was really impressive though, was the clarity of the call. It was just as if my ex wife was in the next phone booth – a scenario that made the hairs stand up on the back of my neck and beads of sweat form on my brow. I said my goodbyes and promised them a variety of presents – all made from dead possums – before flagging down the bus and heading back to my cosy van.

I must admit that the cold night air had made my three quarters of a bottle of Shiraz feel more like three bottles. The entrance to the camp site was wide enough to drive a Winnebago through without a struggle, but I still somehow managed to bounce off both brick columns as I staggered past, like a chromium pinball frantically ricocheting around in one of those arcade bagatelle machines. I was having a lot of trouble locating my van too, because it was extremely dark, and, thanks to Sod's Law, the light that was supposed to be illuminating pitch number sixty-six was the only one out of two hundred that didn't embrace the Protestant work ethic – either that or it was afraid of moths. I made my way around the van to locate the side door, key at the ready, and all of a sudden, my world quite literally turned upside down. I became acutely aware of a searing pain down my left leg, followed by a somersaulting sensation, and then I met the hard earth with a mighty bang. For some reason, I was now flat-out on the ground and looking up at the wonderfully clear night sky, a full moon and a trillion twinkly stars, which ordinarily I would have enjoyed enormously. On this occasion however, I was more concerned about my leg, which felt as if it were snapped in two, such was the pain. Not being overly manly, I emitted a scream similar to that of a feral cat that had been accidentally run over by a Flymo whilst snoozing in the long grass. Jeez, did it hurt. Then, one by one, camper van lights came on, followed by annoyed-looking Germans, Americans, Brits and Australians, peering through curtains to see what was going on. Seconds later, they were joined by the poorer people in the nearby tents, some of whom had crawled out, bleary-eyed to get a better look. One man shone a torch at me, and it was only then that I realized I had fallen over a huge wooden picnic bench. I glanced down at my battered leg to find that there was a sizeable tear in my trousers and red stuff oozing through the gap. Even in my confused state, I knew right away that it wasn't Shiraz; if I could trust my rudimentary grasp of biology, that only ever gets as far as the stomach before being converted to urine. I dragged myself upright and began to mutter inane apologies to the now significant crowd, and I heard at least one shitbag make some snide comment about the English and their drinking. Then, one by one, once they'd done their share of tutting, they crawled back into their tents and vans and tried once more to sleep. My leg was smarting like a bugger now, and felt red-hot. I limped a few yards towards the van, wincing with the pain, and almost tripped over something else beneath my feet. At first I thought I'd trodden on a snake, but I remembered that New Zealand doesn't have any. Then I trod on it again, and all hell broke loose. A powerful jet of cold water blasted me in the face, and once more I was screaming like a banshee. As the van lights came on again, I saw what looked like a huge green serpent rearing up in front of me, blasting water from its mouth. It must have been twelve feet high now, twisting and turning erratically, like a crazed cobra, sending high-pressure jets of water in all directions with the force of one of those water cannons they use in China to quell a peasant uprising. One man crawled out of his tent, and was blasted clean off his feet. Then the serpent turned on the motor home to my right, sending gallons of water through its open windows. An irate German, who was striding over to castigate me was hit full on in the mouth and drenched. Now the serpent had changed tack, and instead of rearing up aggressively, it was whizzing round in circles like a lunatic lasso, expertly taking a lady's legs from under her before she could flatten me with her shovel. Throughout all this, I was trying desperately to work out exactly where this tidal wave was coming from, and it was only when the couple in the van to my left turned on their lights that I could see what on earth had happened. The serpent was plot number sixty-six's high-pressure water hose. The previous occupant of my space hadn't hung it on its wooden post after use, and I'd trodden on the nozzle at the end and twisted the metal lever to 'on'. I limped over to the wooden post and turned the water supply off at the brass tap. Instantly, the serpent fell to the ground and died, but campers situated within a fifteen metre radius of pitch number sixty-six had paid a heavy price.

It was carnage. The water had entered my neighbour's van through his open window and saturated his and his wife's Blue Cod supper. Several tents were uninhabitable. Ordinarily, I'd have made amends there and then, but I was in so much pain that grovelling would have to wait till the next day. I knew I'd have to don the sackcloth and ashes at breakfast and do the rounds, apologizing profusely, but all I really wanted to do at that juncture was repair to my van and whimper. I offered one half-soaked communal 'sorry', accompanied by a general wave and dived inside before I could do anything else to upset them. I did, however, have the presence of mind to quickly check my handbrake before I turned in, just in case. Knowing my luck, I'd have woken up floating down one of those rapid, boulder-strewn rivers, heading for Queenstown.

CHIPTAH 11

*In which I head for Queenstown, the Adventure Capital, and
have a few adventures I hadn't bargained for.*

I seemed to be developing a rather disconcerting habit of
lacerating random sections of my body, before falling asleep and
allowing the resulting blood to weld itself to my bed clothes. Had
it been a new Olympic sport, I would surely have been good
enough for at least a bronze medal. Having earlier practised with
my brow, I had now perfected the art with my leg. I wondered if
they'd had the same trouble at the battle of Wounded Knee, back
in 1890. I wouldn't mind betting that Chief Bigfoot woke up the
day after his ding-dong with General James K. Forsyth with his
leg stuck to his wigwam, if indeed it was his knee that got
wounded. I couldn't comment, as I wasn't there. Either way, if it
hurt half as much as mine did, I feel sorry for him, that's all I can
say.

I made myself a cup of tea, finished off the cornflakes, and
sneaked over to the shower block wearing dark glasses and a false
beard fashioned from possum fur, in order to avoid a conflict that
could easily have led to World War Three. I dived into the shower
cubicle avoiding all eye contact and remembering to lock the door
this time. Then, for six glorious minutes – or one token, in old
money – I luxuriated in the revitalizing hot water, groaning in
ecstasy and soaping myself up, whilst carefully skirting around the
mass of contusions I had collected, which looked like a sort of
human bruise museum.

Ablutions completed, I dashed back to the van. I didn't really want to make myself a target for abuse by stopping to fill up with water and emptying the chemical lavatory, and besides, there wasn't that much poo in it at that point, so I jumped aboard and made a hasty exit. It was now a priority of mine to find the next site, and become one of its model citizens. I would leave it to someone else to get trapped inside a tumble dryer in the laundry, or demolish the barbecue and its customers with his van whilst reversing. I'd done my bit for the time being. I was sick of being Top Tin's very own version of Stan Laurel, thank you very much.

The previous night's trauma had also been responsible for bringing on another of my vivid dreams. This time my motor home was careering down Mount Cook and slamming through flimsy log cabins as it descended, scattering terrified families and their possessions to the four winds. I woke up sweating and needing the lavatory, and it was only then that I realized that I was dragging my blood-stained duvet along with me.

New Zealand seems to possess everything we have in Britain, but sort of jumbled up. Our northern areas, such as the Lake District and the Highlands of Scotland boast snow-capped mountains and lakes – or lochs, as those ginger-haired skirt-wearing haggis-botherers call them, and so does the south of New Zealand. I rolled into the Mount Cook Visitors' Centre after the usual, glorious scenic drive, and parked the van. Hundreds of Japanese tourists had just arrived in a fleet of luxury coaches and they were busy camcordering and photographing each other, the coaches, the mountains, the public lavatories and the statue of Sir Edmund Hillary. Sir Edmund's sculptor had even chiselled a look of displeasure into the chap's face, as if he were anticipating the hundreds of camera-happy Japanese that the great man would one day have to endure. The mountaineer seemed to be gritting his teeth as if in discomfort, and if it wasn't the visitors that were causing it, my second guess would have been that his privates had become completely frozen while up Everest, and old Edmund was too much of a man to scream out loud like I had a habit of doing.

136

I fancied a bit of a walk, so I set off along the path towards the mountain, along with several of the Japanese tourists. What most people never realize is that you can't just start climbing these mountains as soon as you get out of the car park. Often, there's a two mile walk just to get to the official start of the thing. It's not just a flat field with a sudden vertical piece of rock jutting out of it, and signs that say, 'Mountain starts here' with arrows pointing skywards. I've actually climbed the famous 'three peaks' in Britain, so I know. I must explain that I climbed them at a rate of one per year, as opposed to all three in one weekend, like some nutters do, but even so, I conquered them and that's something you can't take away from me. The thing with these mountains is, they go on and on and on, and then on some more. I'd meet walkers coming down and ask them breathlessly, 'How far to the top?' and they'd say, 'Oh, about forty minutes left.' Then, forty minutes later, I'd meet more walkers and ask, 'How far to the top?' and they'd say, 'Oh, I'd estimate around forty minutes.' Well, this is nothing short of soul-destroying; it saps the spirit, but you soldier on regardless, gritting your teeth like the statue of Sir Edmund. Exhausted now, you round a corner and greet several elated walkers who have just been to the top, and you ask – nay, beg of them – 'How far to the summit, mate?' and one of them replies, 'Oh, not far now. About an hour, at a guess.'

When I climbed Ben Nevis it took four and a half hours. I began the walk in sunny weather, which became overcast and drizzly. By the time I had reached the top, we were in arctic conditions and standing in two feet of snow. I was with my brother, Steve, and we feared we may have to eat each other. Well, Mount Cook is three times higher than that, and Everest is nearly three times higher than *that!* I reached the end of the path where the mountain began, and that was enough for me. I turned around and headed for the car park and a cup of tea.

The tearoom was predictably crowded with Japs snapping each other's cakes with their Nikons, so I decided against it and headed off in search of adventure, otherwise known as Queenstown. After a trouble-free night spent at Omarama, for which I was truly grateful, and another at the beautiful Lake Wanaka, which was nothing short of a miracle given my track record of late, I began my winding descent into Queenstown. If you will recall, I made a solemn promise to quit enthusing about views every five minutes unless they were exceptional, but I make no apology for returning to the subject at this point. I jumped out of the motor home near the top of the mountains in order to take a look down the valley at this most scenic of towns and the blue sea behind it. I could instantly understand why Peter Jackson had chosen the area as a backdrop for his Lord of the Rings trilogy. It was like Wales and Scotland rolled into one, but even more dramatic somehow. Then I saw the Japanese coaches pull into the lay-by behind me – the same ones I had encountered back at Mount Cook. Within a few seconds, they'd all piled out and were taking pictures, not of the views, but of each other in front of their coaches. Some had ventured away from the group and were taking snaps of a dull old sign that said 'look-out point'. It reminded me of a cartoon idea I once came up with, depicting one of those commemorative benches in a pretty park. The bench, instead of facing the rolling parkland and lake, was instead facing a twelve-foot high brick wall. The brass plaque on the bench read;

In loving memory of Alf Spittle – Bricklayer.

He loved this view

I jumped back on board and headed for town, down a zigzag road with a sheer drop to one side that would have encouraged even James Bond to fill his boxers. I found the good old Top Tin and parked up for the night, relieved that it hadn't cost me fifty dollars this time. I had dreaded the thought of this trip since I walked out of Mr Chance's offices, but now I felt more alive than I had felt since I was a child. I intended to stay a few nights in Queenstown and I couldn't wait to explore. I won't say that I had become a thrill-seeker as such, but I certainly felt up to *watching* people throwing themselves off cliffs, leaping from planes and battling ferocious rivers. Prior to this trip, my idea of living dangerously had been to order food and not ask what the salad contained. Oh, and I did answer my ex-wife honestly once when she asked if her bum looked big in a pair of trousers she'd recently acquired. Now, all of a sudden, I was actually feeling like a bit of a fraud, travelling all the way to Queenstown and not doing something I could brag about when I got home. Maybe there were 'not-so extreme' sports you could sign up for, like jumping off a low step into something a bit wet, or perhaps riding a quad bike along a strip of wide tarmac and having to avoid a plastic cone, or a stuffed possum, maybe. Then I could say I'd entered into the spirit of the place.

It was, then, something of a surprise to find myself wandering down town before dinner and marching into the ticket shop to book a ride on the Shotover Jet boat. I still have no idea what came over me. I hadn't even been drinking, though I intended to have one just afterwards over dinner to calm the nerves. I suppose the rationale behind my impulsive behaviour, if there was any, was that I was beginning to realize what a couch potato I had become, and I think I was finally beginning to understand why my uncle had done this to me. At first, I'd likened him to a wicked puppet master, pulling my strings from beyond the grave, humiliating me and making me participate in silly challenges in return for my reward, like a dog sitting up and begging for a titbit. In reality, his plan, I now felt sure, was far more altruistic. He was reminding me to live before I died, as he had done.

I once became very irate, for associated reasons, with a man I vaguely knew, when he criticized one of my brother's plays. The mealy-mouthed little shit just carped on for ages in the bar at the half-time interval until I cut across him and asked him how *his* new play was coming on. He, of course, replied that he wasn't writing one, and I explained to him that this was because he'd never done anything with his miserable life except slag off those who had actually got off their arses, like brother Steve had done, burning the midnight oil, writing, rewriting, honing and perfecting every line, before recruiting, rehearsing and paying actors for months on end, all for three nights of misery, caused by prats like this bloke pissing all over what should have been my brother's proudest moment. Things turned decidedly frosty after that, and he pretended that he had to go to the bar to buy peanuts. Well, what I think I was trying to say just now was that people who *do* stuff are often criticized, but at least they do stuff. Sometimes it might be good, and other times not, but at least they're trying to achieve something and that's what counts. Look at my old mate Paul McCartney for example. He wrote *Hey Jude*, *The Long and Winding Road*, *Here, There and Everywhere*, *She's Leaving Home*, *Get Back*, *Let It Be*, *Yesterday*, and hundreds more. In my book, that lets him off the hook for the *Frog Chorus* and *Ebony and Ivory*. Uncle Ken saw that I was becoming the theatre critic instead of the playwright, so he deliberately set up my Big Adventure, and boy was I loving it; apart from, of course, the hotel murder, the handcuffs, the heroin smuggling, the 'Maori in the Shaori', the busted knee and the water cannon incident. Even those had their place, now that the initial trauma had subsided. They were now filed under 'Great Anecdotes To Regale People With For The Rest Of My Life', and that, surely, was a good thing. Already I was chuckling to myself about some of them, though not about poor old Herr Fuchs of course. I'm not a sicko.

I traipsed around Queenstown looking for a nice restaurant and there were quite a few to choose from. The harbour area boasted several, but most were seafood places which make me a bit squeamish sometimes. I passed a diner who was getting to grips with a thing that resembled the face-hugger in Alien, and it kind of put me off, so I went to an Italian instead. There were pizzas on offer, but I wasn't going to commit until I'd seen one, so I ordered a glass of red and perused the menu, stalling for time. Eventually, one came out of the kitchen, and predictably it was the MDF biscuit variety, so I went for the pasta instead. I couldn't understand how an Italian chef could emigrate to New Zealand and then forget everything he'd ever learnt about the noble art of pizza making. Then the waitress arrived at my table, and it all became clear. Everyone in the joint was Eastern European. If

140

they'd ever been to Italy, it was only to pass through en route to somewhere else that was softer on immigrants. This led me on to another train of thought. How many Italian restaurants are actually run by Italians, I wondered. My local one in Stourbridge was owned by an Indian, though he did have a pet Italian that he wheeled out to look good and charm the women occasionally, or explain what 'al dente' meant to the ones who complained that their pasta was underdone. The Italian nearby in Six Ashes was owned by a Greek. The one I liked that closed down in Kingswinford was run by an English girl and a chap from Turkey, and one that I regularly visited in Birmingham was actually ninety per cent Welsh, if you can believe that. Maybe their signature dish was Spaghetti 'Western', or perhaps Penne 'Bont'.

That aside, a pretty girl is a pretty girl in any language, and what my waitress lacked in Italianness, she made up for in looks, to the point where I would have gladly eaten an MDF pizza off a dirty floor if she'd asked me to. I even fooled myself into imagining she quite liked me too, but she was probably like that with all the punters. These Eastern Europeans will do anything for a big tip, so to speak. She wiggled off with my order and delivered my wine a few minutes later. I swear she winked at me as well, but that might just have been wishful winking on my part.

As usual, I was tucked away in Johnny-No-Mates Corner, and all of a sudden, I did feel lonely and a long way from home. I don't know if you've ever had to eat alone, but it's no fun. You find yourself trying to make it last longer by ordering more things than you really want to eat, and I tend to drink a bit too much as well. The previous couple of days had been so hectic, what with one thing and another, that I hadn't really had time to ponder this, but now I was more relaxed and feeling up to a spot of company. I've never chatted a girl up in my life, as I might or might not have mentioned, but a new boldness had entered my soul. Maybe it was because I was so far away from home, so if, or rather, when, I made a fool of myself, no one would find out. Perhaps it was the glass of grappa I'd ordered to round off my meal and waste

141

another twenty minutes which had sent me over the edge, or even the spirit of Uncle Ken taking me over. Whatever it was, I resolved to ask this girl if she was up to anything after her shift, and if not, would she care to pop along to a bar and grab a beer with me, as I believe the cool expression is. She came over with my bill and I stood up to meet her halfway, ejecting a spare sock from my trouser leg as I did so. I was wondering where it had got to. She spotted it and began to giggle, which did make me feel rather like an imbecile. I apologized for my unkempt appearance, explaining that I was in a motor home. I told her that I needed a woman in my life to control my socks, which were wild, and often hid in trousers to evade capture. Okay, it was gibberish, but she seemed amused by it nevertheless. She retrieved the malodorous object and handed it back, pegging her cute nose with the other hand, and I'm positive that she deliberately stroked my wrist in the process. It was then that I made my move. I asked the question whilst staring at the carpet tiles and making a circling movement on the floor with my right foot.

'You are kidding!' she sneered. 'I'm a lesbian, just like Geisha you bloody loser!'

Actually, she didn't say that. That was me imagining what she would probably say. What she *actually* said was, 'Okay. I'm off in half an hour, so I'll meet you down town at the Flat Possum Bar.'

I just smiled dumbly, and I may have drooled a little from the corner of my mouth. I just hoped she hadn't spotted it.

After a very pleasant, chatty hour at the Flat Possum, in which consumed even more alcohol to calm my nerves, we got to the awkward moment when it was time to get up and go. My mind was in turmoil. Did I ask her to visit my passion wagon back at the Top Tin, or did we merely have a bit of a snog outside and say 'G'day'? I was just rummaging around in the recesses of my fuddled brain for the least smarmy way of raising the subject when she looked into my bloodshot eyes and spoke.

'Let's go back to your motor home and make love!' she grinned, as shamelessly as if she were asking me to play Monopoly with her.

'Oh, erm, okay, erm, lovely!' I spluttered, my heart doing cartwheels.

We left the Flat Possum arm in arm and staggered up the hill. I don't know who had left that hill there, but it was most inconsiderate, I thought. It certainly wasn't there when I walked down that long slope into the town earlier. By the time I got to the top I was a spent force, and there was still a decent walk ahead of us to the camp site. All the way there, she kept rubbing bits of me that hadn't been rubbed for some time, and by the time I stood fumbling with my keys in the dark, having first checked carefully that there was no bench to fall over, I must have resembled Terry, the Human Tripod. I don't know if you've ever tried to open a motor home door in a pitch black camp site with a raging erection in your pants and a Croatian waitress tonguing your ear, but let me assure you that it is not as easy as it sounds, if indeed it does sound easy. She'd got more tentacles than an octopus, or any other creature that has tentacles, for that matter. Once inside, we stumbled around in the dark and eventually fell onto the seats that turned into my bed. I suggested that she calm down for half a minute while I made it up, and even then she couldn't keep her hands off me. Very flattering, of course, but boy was she impatient!

I did the best I could, but I'd never made the bed in the dark, so when we dived onto it, it collapsed onto the floor. Sensing that she wouldn't allow more wasted time, we continued where we'd ended up. Then my phone rang. I explained that it might well be very important, so I flicked on a small sidelight, pulled the phone from my pocket and answered it. Miss Croatia, meanwhile, carried on molesting me like a female Praying Mantis, while I tried with all the willpower at my disposal to remain *compos mentis*.

It was Fu Manchu.

'Ah, Mr Eve, have I caught you at an inconvenient time?' he asked dryly.

'No, not at all,' I lied. Miss Croatia set about exploring my underpants while she was waiting.

'I just wanted to fill you in on what we've discovered so far,' he continued.

'Very thoughtfoo-oo-oh of you,' I replied, gesturing wildly for her to take a breather.

'The CCTV footage has now been examined,' he explained, 'we have identified the two men, but their faces are not visible, I'm afraid.'

'Oh, oh, oh my God, I'm oh, sorry to hear that,' I gasped.

'Mr Eve,' he interjected, 'are you feeling okay? You sound very strange.'

'Er, no, I have, erm, severe food poisoning I'm afraid. I keep having to be sick or dash to the lavatory.'

Miss Croatia gave me a worried look, but I managed to convey to her in one complex and indescribable gesture that I was lying. She seemed satisfied by this and began to demonstrate her uncanny impression of a Henry vacuum cleaner.

'I'm sorry to hear that,' said Fu Manchu. 'You must now replace your bodily fluids. That is most important. Have you been eating seafood?'

'Not ye-e-e-t, but I hope to,' I answered.

'Then make sure what you eat is fresh and well washed. You cannot be too careful.'

'I'll bear that in mi-ooo-nd,' I promised him. 'Look, would you-oo-oo mind ringing back tomorroo-jeez? I should be better by then, unless of course I die.'

The policeman said that he would ring again but only if there was more to report, and hung up. Then she really got started.

CHIPTAH 12

*In which I compare Miss Croatia with the Shotover Jet Boat -
with unexpected results.*

What is it with me and nymphomaniacs? I seem to attract them,
like a human Nymphomagnet Maniac. Or did I mean a
Nymphomaniac Magnet? I'll bet you a hundred pounds that any
red-blooded male reading this down the pub will say to his mates,
'I wish I could bloody well find one!' or 'what a way to die!' or
some such tosh. Well, let me tell you, it is absolutely no fun. I've
encountered one before. It was the night I got on a train to
Dartmouth dressed in a pantomime horse outfit. Look, it's a long
story, but suffice it to say that this seemingly prim and proper
business woman on her way back from a convention, was in fact a
danger to mankind, and the most insatiable creature on the planet,
with the possible exception of Miss bloody Croatia, or Gabria, to
give you her proper name. You see, I did bother to ask, and it's
stuck in my mind because if you write it backwards it actually
spells *Airbag*, which is somehow appropriate. Like all men, I like
to have sex, and I'm not ashamed about that. Once is nice, twice –
with a reasonable recovery time – is even better, and I've even
been known to do it three times, when I was in the first flush of
youth. However, if the young lady in question were then to
demand satisfaction yet again, I am prone to look askance. If – and
follow my argument closely here – a woman were to permanently
forego the pie and mash and make herself vomit in the loo every
time she was forced to eat more than a smoked salmon blini at a

147

cocktail party, people would rightly assess that she had a form of bulimia, and suggest she saw a psychiatrist. Conversely, if she weighed the same as a narrow boat and thought nothing of scoffing eighteen iced buns before she got out of bed each day, it could be argued that she was a compulsive eater, and she should contact Weight Watchers pronto, before she exploded. Well surely, Your Honour, a lady who continually wants to have sex but is never satisfied is similarly afflicted, only with her, it isn't seven-inch iced buns she's after. Same mental problem – different stimulus. These people are not wired properly. They never seem to know when they are full up, and I choose the phrase advisedly.

Anyway, I'm far too much of a gentleman to go into the sordid details, so if that's what you were looking forward to, I'm sorry to disappoint you. Suffice it to say that at precisely seven-thirty-six the next morning, I was, to all intents and purposes, a dried husk, incapable of walking in a straight line or speaking coherently. To be quite honest, it had put me off seeking further female companionship while I was Down Under, and that's another phrase I chose deliberately. If I ever do attempt to explain what I went through, using my finely-honed literary skills, I may well call the piece, 'Down Under Down Under'. I made a mental note to buy a snorkel, just in case – heaven forbid – it ever happened again.

I offered the girl a slice of toast and a cup of tea, but she didn't want either. Perhaps she got her protein in other ways; I don't know. She made her excuses and flitted off, as fresh as a daisy, presumably to get her daily sexual fix from some other unsuspecting mug who'd just arrived in the Adventure Capital.

After an hour spent staring at the seat opposite, with not a single thought echoing around in my head, I eventually rallied around enough to make it to the shower block, where I spent three tokens in an attempt to kick-start my system. Even this began disastrously, due to the fact that I'd hastily grabbed the soap from the draining board in my motor home, wrapping it in my towel, and was initially puzzled as to why it generated absolutely no lather. It was only after closer examination that I realized I had been coating my naked body with a stale block of cheddar cheese, discarded from Tuesday's cheese and biscuits session. Luckily, the previous occupant of my cubicle had generously left behind a soggy sliver of Imperial Leather with entwined pubic hair, which I was reluctantly and squeamishly forced to use. Otherwise I'd have been one of the few campers in history to emerge from a hot, invigorating shower smelling considerably worse than when he went in. Feeling a little better now in both body and spirit (in spite of my rather disappointing bathing experience), I wandered down town to the booking office, where I was to catch the coach to Shotover Canyon.

Half an hour of windy road and dramatic scenery later, we fetched up at the car park, where we were met by the guides who explained to us that anyone who had a heart condition or was pregnant or had just been having sex for eight hours solid, had to fill in a form, signing over all property and possessions in the event of death. Then we were taken to the visitor centre until our boat was ready, where we mooched around, looking at framed pictures of celebrities such as Sir Ian Botham, Alanis Morisette and a bloke from a soap opera whose name escapes me, standing proudly in front of the jet boat, presumably seconds before it reunited them with their breakfasts. We could also watch the official video while we were waiting, but I chose not to.

Paperwork concluded, we were fitted with life jackets and given a quick safety talk. It was all common sense really. Don't try to play backgammon during the trip, don't try touching the boulders with the tip of your nose as they whiz by at seventy miles per hour, and definitely don't clasp your hands around the driver's eyes for a giggle and say 'Guess who?'

We climbed aboard what looked like a red powerboat that had been put together by a couple of NASA engineers in their lunch break, with bits they had left over from a space shuttle. Unlike normal speed boats, it was designed to cope with shallow water, often less than a foot deep, to be precise, and it was also unfazed by lumpy rocks, dead sheep or supermarket trolleys. The canyon was a picturesque, boulder-strewn affair, with fast-flowing water, like the places those demented canoeists seem to favour. Think *Deliverance* with Burt Reynolds and you wouldn't be far off. Apparently, there were two such jetboats, with a team of around four or five drivers, if that is the correct term, and they all have to take intensive courses in order to learn how best to scare the shit out of people without actually killing anyone. They also have to be christened Brett, Shane, Kyle or Wayne, and have nerves of steel. My driver was called Shane, and it was rumoured that he was the best of the bunch; the only one qualified to execute the three-sixty upside down triple toe-loop with a blindfold on, under water. At least, I think that's what they said. I was too full of trepidation to listen.

Shane introduced himself to us, instructed us to strap ourselves in, and then rocketed away like a bat out of hell towards a gap between two huge boulders that didn't, to my untrained eye, look anywhere near wide enough for us to get through. Even the Japanese on board decided against getting their cameras or personal belongings out, though I'm sure I saw one elderly gentleman's false teeth come flying past me. Either that or it was his previously digested prawn sandwich on white. Shane seemed to be as relaxed as if he were driving his Ford Escort into the Asda car park, and quite oblivious to the fact that he was approaching two immovable objects, sideways-on at seventy, with not a cat's chance of getting through them in one piece. I swear he was even chatting to a passenger as he did so. Then the boat powered through with no more than two inches clearance either side. I tried to scream, but my scream seemed too scared to come out into the open, and had gone off to hide somewhere near my arse. Then, before I could get my bearings, the boat was spinning full circle at vicious speed, so that we were briefly able to admire the two boulders once more, before most of the bones that held our heads in place succumbed to the violent whiplash and collapsed like Jenga blocks.

'How was thit?' asked Shane, nonchalantly as you like. Those whose heads hadn't yet sunken into their ribcages gibbered in unison. Then, interpreting our incoherent pleas for mercy as tacit approval, he *really* let rip, careering off down the river aiming for boulders, and then missing them at the last second – and I mean the last second. It then dawned on me why they needed two boats. It must have taken the cleaners ages to fumigate one after an outing, so they alternated them to save time. To mix things up, every now and again he would spin the boat a full three-sixty or pull up extremely suddenly to comment on a view, before once more hammering the throttle and pointing the thing at a sheer rock face, as if it were a guided missile. All this would be bad enough on a road, with a professional stunt driver at the helm, but rivers have a mind of their own, and are full of unknown hazards. I genuinely think that old Shane knew precisely where every single rock was hidden – he was that good. The advertising blurb in the Shotover Jet leaflet stated that there had been no accidents in all their years of operation. I take it they meant major ones, because I felt sure the chap next to me had just had one, and he couldn't have been the first.

Strangely, I loved every mad minute of it. I trusted Shane implicitly, and even when he turned around to smile inanely at us as his boat appeared to be a split second from disintegration, I knew he'd spin it around in the nick of time and thrill us again, before he finally headed back to the start point. I'd now had two white-knuckle rides in the space of twelve hours, and it was still only eleven-thirty.

And guess what. Miss Croatia was definitely scarier, and after our third coupling, not half as much fun. Mind you, after sixteen jet boat excursions, maybe I would have revised my opinion once more. I don't know. At least Miss Croatia was free, whereas the boat was twenty quid a pop, so the likelihood of me going on it more than once was remote.

I arrived back at the booking offices at lunchtime clutching my commemorative DVD, T-shirt and toy jet boat made from possum

151

fur, and, in the heat of the moment, I almost signed up for something else. The trouble was, everything involved leaping from a great height and shouting 'Geronimo!' and I didn't do heights, unless I was encapsulated by something. Even then, I hated it, so it came as something of a surprise when I found myself heading for the gondolas, so that I could come down the mountain on a thing that looked like a tea tray with a handbrake. Okay, compared to bungee-jumping off a railway bridge into a mile-deep canyon with snapping crocodiles at the bottom, it was tame stuff, but at least I was trying to get into the spirit of the place.

The gondolas are small egg-shaped glass compartments with four seats that take you up a mountain to the visitors' centre at the top, and they're not for the squeamish. Occasionally, the operator, who was a sadistic bastard called Wayne, or Shane, or Brett, or Kyle, deliberately stops your progress, and you just sway in the wind and creak a lot, half a mile in the sky, convinced the thing has broken down and you are doomed. You stop breathing, and desperately try to read the other passengers' facial expressions to see if they look worried. You instantly notice that they aren't breathing either, and they're staring back at you, with clammy beads of sweat forming on their brows. Unless, of course, they are Japanese, in which case they're too busy photographing each other to care. Then, after three minutes of this hell, the rusty cables creak into action once more and you continue onwards and upwards, to infinity and beyond. The other thing I love about these gondolas is the fact that you are forced to leap out of them when you get to the top, as they are not programmed to stop. I imagined taking my grandmother on one and having to watch her go round the system until she died.

Having leapt, gazelle-like, to safety, I walked immediately to the viewing point to see where I had travelled from, and flipping heck, I was high up. If all the views I had seen thus far had to be marked out of ten – or tin – then this was surely a perfect tin. Words, for once, fail me. You just had to be there. I walked through the turnstile, blowing a poisoned dart into Wayne's neck as he sat in his control room, chortling to himself at the images on his CCTV of terrified punters clutching their chests. Satisfied that he now only had seconds to live, I pressed on to the terrace at the back, where I located the steps to the luge track. Brett, the luge operator, sat me down on my tea tray and explained the brake mechanism to me in great detail.

'G'day! Shove the stick this way, it goes *really* fast. Pull it this way, it goes faster still.'

At least, I think that's what he said. To be honest, I wasn't listening. It's a bit like when you stop someone in the street to ask directions. As soon as they open their mouth, you sort of switch off, and you're no wiser after you've driven away. I wasn't duly worried, however, as there were only two positions, so I was bound to be able to sort it out myself, by trial and error.

There were two tracks, the beginners' and the advanced, and you had to go down the easy one before you were entitled to go on the other one. I careered off like a thing possessed, hitting the first bend at around two hundred miles per hour, still desperately trying to fathom out what, if anything, the stick did. Then, as I belted down the straight, sparks flying from my rear end, I was confronted by a gaggle of Japanese tourists who had somehow found their way onto the bobsleigh track and were shooting footage of each other. I screamed for them to bugger off sharpish, but they seemed to be frozen, like rabbits in the headlamps. Impact now seemed inevitable, and so it was. I took one middle-aged gentleman's legs from under him, and the next thing I know, he was lying down like a dead possum behind me, twenty feet away. Luckily, I escaped without serious injury, if you discount the bruised eye his Nikon digital gave me as he flew over my head. It was hanging on a strap around his neck when he took off. I was far too concerned with my own safety to spend too much time looking back, but I did see his colleagues trying to drag him off before another tea tray got him. When I reached the bottom, I dropped my luge onto the automatic retrieval system and stormed off to see the chap in the lower kiosk, in order to warn him before someone got killed. He located the lunatics on his CCTV monitor and groaned, 'Jesus Christ!' before handing me my token for the advanced track.

'Have another go at the stupid bastards, mate,' he continued, 'and you get a free ride if you get a strike, like in tin pin bowling!'

I climbed back up the steps, nursing my second black eye in as many weeks, and got to the top just in time to see several security guards escorting the party away from the track, followed by two St. John's Ambulance types struggling down the grassy slope with a stretcher. The stricken victim it was carrying was sitting up, taking pictures of his rescuers, so that he could show his family back in Tokyo how he'd broken both his ankles.

I whizzed down the advanced track, screeching around the corners whilst singing 'All Right Now' by *Free* as loud as I could, and I can honestly say that I'd seldom felt happier. Even the realization that I'd probably put some poor tourist in hospital and ruined his holiday couldn't dampen my spirits.

I stayed in Queenstown for another day, avoiding the Italian restaurant and the Flat Possum Bar like the plague, and then I slowly headed towards Picton, where the car ferry leaves for North Island, trying to take in as many attractions as I could en-route. I saw, as Howard Carter famously remarked upon first glimpsing King Tut's tomb, 'Wonderful things!' I stood on a freezing cold beach at twilight watching gaggles of cute penguins coming home after a hard day's fishing. I observed lazy seals lolloping around on the rocks. I went out to sea to observe majestic Sperm whales diving into the abyss, and I watched dolphins dance around our boat, showing off for all they were worth. It was all fantastic of course, but just like England – with its Paperweight Centre and Barometer World, to name but two of many – there were some dubious attractions too. Studying my expensive map, I picked out, with a view to avoidance, such gems as the Giant Bottle (North Island), which appeared to be a nothing more or less than a large fibre-glass bottle advertising the local brewer's wares. It was sited in some God-forsaken town with a name like Wanapuanawiwi, for the benefit of people to gawp at on Sundays, when there wasn't much else to do. I'd recently driven through a pleasant enough one-horse town called Ranfurly, which boasted a plethora of important Art Deco buildings, according to my guide book, and unless the term means something completely different in New Zealand, I think the local mayor had slipped the publication a back-hander. I am quite au fait with the Art Deco style, and I never spotted a single place worthy of mention, by English standards at least. I suppose, when other places are offering dolphins, whales and penguins in order to siphon off the tourist dollar, you have to use whatever means you have at your disposal to get the punters to visit you, but this smacked of desperation. What next? Visit Wangawongatonga, home of the autistic savant sheep, Waynetta, who regularly astounds visitors with her grasp of quadratic equations? (But she does have to be in the mood.)

Then there were the Giant Spherical Stones, which were advertised as if they were the eighth wonder of the world, and, joy of joys, I happened to be driving straight past them anyway. I pulled in, full of nervous anticipation, paid my donation and descended the steps to the beach to find five or six, four-foot high spherical stones on the sand, minding their own business. Maybe I was missing something. Maybe there were colossal ones just around the next cove, standing fifty feet high. The stones were undoubtedly unusual, I'll grant you that, but I wouldn't have built a day around them. Call me a Philistine, but even Stonehenge is only worth ten minutes. There was a purpose-built visitors' centre and leaflets explaining how they might have got there. I wouldn't have put it past the town council to have had them sculpted out of concrete and sprayed with something to make them look old. Maybe that's what the leaflets said, but I didn't bother to get one. For some inexplicable reason, all I could think of as I beat a hasty retreat was *Father Ted* – the episode where the funfair comes to Craggy Island. The only difference was; at least the attractions on offer there were funny.

By the time I rolled into Picton, I had been in New Zealand for almost two weeks, and it was feeling just like home; comfortable, like an old shoe, even though, in terms of countries, the place could never be thought of as old. If anything, this was my only gripe with the place. I felt that if I lived there, I would be forfeiting all the rich and wonderful heritage of Great Britain. Here was a country that thought Art Deco was ancient, and Victorian was virtually Stone Age. Also, I had rather hoped that the country would follow England's lead with regard to architecture and style, but apart from places like Christchurch, it seemed to be getting its ideas from the U.S.A, which I thought misguided and a little sad. Even the currency was dollars and cents, which, in my eyes, was tantamount to treason. I just hoped that one day they'd see sense, ditch the tacky Yanks and come home to Blighty, spiritually speaking.

Picton was just lovely. There was a delightful, palm tree-lined front with a tiny beach area, and a handful of cafés, restaurants and shops. People were sitting in the sunshine watching the big ferries come and go, picking their way carefully through a maze of verdant islands, just as Captain Cook had done when he discovered the place all those years ago, *en route* for the North Island. Power boats scudded across the brilliant turquoise waters towing water-skiers behind them, and way up high in the hills, the residents gazed down on God's creation from their glass-fronted, minimalist, designer-built cabins and no doubt wondered to themselves, 'Have we died and gone to heaven?'

After parking up at the Top Tin – God bless them – I spent a lazy day mooching around in Picton, my base until eight-thirty the following morning, when I was due to drive onto a ferry and sail north to begin the second leg of my trip.

The phone rang that evening, as I was halfway through my Blue Cod. It was Tina, of Tina's Travel, with very exciting news. Inspector Clouseau had been into the shop again, and my Aussie friend, Jake, had been summoned post-haste to act as the unsuspecting traveller. True to form, two days later, Jake had been visited by two police officers fitting the description, and asked to take part in a bit of undercover drug smuggling. Unfortunately for the ugly twins, Jake's room had been wired up with microphones and secret cameras, and as soon as they had concluded their interview, several burly constables leapt out of every available cavity swinging their truncheons and shouting, 'You're nicked, my san!'

Apparently, according to Jake, it was all very exhilarating indeed, and he wouldn't have missed it for the world. Now, thanks to a bit of police brutality, the two had coughed up, spilled the beans, grassed or cried like babies, depending on which cliché you prefer, and the whole evil empire was beginning to fall like a deck of cards. They had even handed over the names of their murdering accomplices in Singapore, in the vain hope that it would reduce their sentences by a few years.

Tina did also mention that the English police wanted to have a quiet word in my shell-like when I returned, partly to thank me, of course, but also to give me a bollocking for being so stupid in the first place. I gave Tina Fu Manchu's number, and asked her to pass it to the boys in blue. I figured that it would gain me valuable Brownie points and reduce the severity of my telling off. It was a vain hope, to be honest. The police just love to give us a good telling off, don't you find? You may have thought that what *really* gets them going is a good car chase, or a sting operation resulting in the capture of fifteen hard-nosed East End criminals, but no – you are mistaken. What really floats their boat – to use an expression I don't even like so I'm surprised I just used it – is a drearily worthy, condescending, po-faced, treat-you-like-an-idiot, humourless, badly phrased, pedestrian, CSE Grade Six sarcastic, telling off. And what's worse, you have to eat humble pie and take it on the chin, because if you get the least bit arsey, or dare to remind them that you've got a very good degree from wherever-it-was-you-went, and you're not only ten times more intelligent but better at sarcasm than they are, they'll just have the last laugh and give you a ticket, or ask you to produce your documents at some obscure, far-away police station in the Hebrides, arrest you for insolence, or even beat the living shit out of you. All things considered, it's just easier to suffer their diatribe for five minutes and say thank you at the end.

Sorry, where was I? Oh yes, it would reduce the severity of my telling off, but far more importantly, I was also keen to see the murderers of an innocent scissor-lift salesman brought to book. Tina promised that she would give Fu Manchu's details to them right away. I made a mental note to purchase a possum product of some sort for her by way of saying thank you. In the meantime, I rang the inscrutable old git myself with the good news, promising him that a collar was imminent. He *seemed* pleased, but it was hard to tell with him. He thanked me politely, before adding that it was not a good idea to tell a pack of lies about Maori carvings to senior Singapore police officers. He also mentioned that – but for the grace of God – I could potentially have been facing a firing squad. I thanked him for his impromptu aural enema, and ended the call. All I needed now was for him to phone back and ask me why there was a pair of sawn-off handcuffs in my hotel lavatory. It was beginning to sound easier all round if I just got myself a house in New Zealand, rather than have to pass through bloody Singapore again on the way back. I hoped that he'd see me in a favourable light for helping him to catch his drug smuggling murderers, rather than cast me into a rat-infested cell full of tattooed psychopaths for having lied to the police and sneaked in six kilos of heroin. It largely depended on if he was a glass half full or a glass half-empty-type I suppose. One thing was for sure though. I'd be packing my bags myself for the return flight.

I decided to get an early night, because I had to be out of the camp site at eight the next morning, and over the past fortnight I'd been waking up later and later. Incidentally, I am convinced that we would all be happier if we abandoned our clocks and watches, woke up when we were ready to and slept when we felt tired. Everything would just level out naturally, as God intended. Surely, it can't be good for the body or spirit to be jerked from our pits by a radio alarm clock each day – especially if the presenter is a complete jerk, as most are. I'm sure it causes cancer or something. I can see a Daily Mail article coming on.

Could Radio Alarm Clocks Cause Cancer?

It's about the only thing The Mail hasn't suspected of it yet. One year it was tomatoes. Then it was electricity pylons, followed by cling film, and mobile phones. Personally, I strongly suspect that the Daily Mail causes cancer, and they're just throwing up these red herrings to put us off the scent. Come to think of it, what about scent? Does that cause cancer? Or what about budgerigars? Those little chirpy bastards aren't as innocent as they'd have us believe, I can tell you.

I rang my family to see if they were missing me, and they just asked, 'Who did you say you were again?' which was mildly amusing. Then I rang mom and dad to see if Len was okay, and mom said he'd been up to his psychic pooing tricks again. The previous evening, he'd spelt out his danger sign, so she was a little concerned. I tried to explain to her that it was only a bit of fun and not to be taken seriously, but he had been spot on with his last few efforts, so now I wasn't so sure. I thanked her for advanced warning, which, if I'm honest, began to play on my mind. Had I not already had my share of slings and arrows? What on earth was coming next, I wondered.

CHIPTAH 13

In which I discover that pretending to be Italian is the best way to retrieve borrowed goods.

At seven-forty-five in the morning, shortly after being woken up with a start by a New Zealand radio presenter with the voice of a buzz saw and the brain of a mackerel, I stood outside the dump station, covered from head to toe in my own shit. Things didn't get much better than that. I had removed my chemical lavatory from it's compartment with a view to emptying it before it caused a cholera epidemic, and rather foolishly I decided to blast it with the high pressure hose to clean the inside of the thing, as it was beginning to stink to high heaven. What I didn't realize was that the contents would just come straight back at me and pebble dash every square inch of my body, minutes after I'd spent my last token in the shower block.

I now had the stark choice of walking into reception in that state, and purchasing another six tokens, or braving the motor home's shower, which only got warm enough to use every eight weeks, and then only for forty seconds. Then there was the question of my attire, which even Baldrick wouldn't have been seen dead in. It was shaping up to be a really good day.

I arrived at the ferry smelling not of shit, but of Lynx, by which I mean the mens' deodorant; not the wild cat. I'd already virtually emptied the bottle of aftershave my daughter bought me for Christmas, and I was beginning to realize that I'd somewhat overcompensated, especially when several of the sailors began to show an unhealthy interest. I parked up and made my way to the decks to grab a tea and a Danish pastry. The lady handed them to me, sniffing the air like a rat as she did so.

'Kin you smill thit?' she asked her colleague with a frown.

'Yis,' replied her colleague, gagging. 'Ask Britt to close the bog door. He always overdoes it with those blue scinted blocks that he drops in the urinals. Pirsonally, I'd rather smill the piss, I really would!'

I grabbed my breakfast and scurried off to my lonely corner, hoping that no one would engage me in conversation until I'd been up on deck for an hour in the stiff breeze.

The ship set sail bang on time, and as we wended our way through the many islands in search of open sea, the captain made an announcement on the intercom. Apparently, it was the fortieth anniversary of the Wahine Ferry disaster of 1968, when Cyclone Giselle joined another huge incoming storm over Wellington, with terrible consequences. The ferry, carrying six hundred and ten passengers and one hundred and twenty-three crew, sank with great loss of life. We were to moor briefly at the spot and lay a floral tribute.

I can't tell you how this announcement made me feel. It was a bit like being on a 747 somewhere high over the Indian Ocean in the middle of the night, and listening to Captain Jim Laidback informing us that it was at this very second, forty years ago, when this very same scheduled flight to New Zealand mysteriously fell out of the sky, killing all on board. Talk about a confidence booster! All of a sudden, I was studying the sky for evidence of storm clouds, and reliving those horrible scenes from Titanic, when old Leonardo di Caprio is handcuffed to railings down in the hold. I know all about handcuffs, let me tell you, and I've grown to hate them. Beads of sweat were breaking out all over my brow just thinking about it.

We eventually reached Wellington Harbour and the ship dropped anchor for twenty minutes, while the ceremony took place. Everyone was on deck, camcordering like they were Japanese, and a flotilla of assorted boats joined us to pay their respects. It was all rather moving, especially when the floral tributes were thrown into the drink and slowly sank. I was minded of the scenes back home in Stourbridge, where every fast road has a bouquet sellotaped to a lamppost or tree, though the circumstances couldn't have been more different. The local Stourbridge youths, clad in their regulation shell suits, baseball caps, sovereign rings and gold chains, go out in their Fiestas on a Friday night, and by Saturday morning they've metamorphosed into a bunch of plastic flowers. The local newspaper then tells us what loveable rogues they were, how they loved a pint with their mates, and enjoyed watching Top Gear on the telly. Usually, the paper plays down the twenty-five Bacardi Breezers, the ninety-mile-an-hour car chase, and the fact that the victim, if that is the right word, also slaughtered an innocent middle-aged couple with a ten-year-old son and a newborn baby – just in case it upsets Wayne the Chav's family.

A lone trumpeter on a tugboat played the Last Post, and then we all sailed into Wellington feeling a bit subdued. I drove off the ferry and onto the ring road, where I circulated manically for an hour or two before spotting the sign I wanted. My next stop was Lake Taupo, which looked a long way off on the map. Wrongly or rightly, I'd been advised that what lay between Wellington and the lake didn't amount to much in the scheme of things, when there were so many better things to see further north. Apparently, the landscape was quite barren, like the Yorkshire moors, and perfect for army exercises, which explained why there were so many bases around there. I'd become quite adept at guessing how long a destination would take to reach, and I didn't fancy making Taupo in one go, so instead I aimed for Wanganui, which appeared to be a sizeable town. I'd been driving for ages and getting a tad delirious, so I pulled into a scenic mountain lay-by to take a rest. I was rummaging through my bag in search of tissues, when I spotted Uncle Ken's pack of letters. I'd been so occupied since I'd arrived in the country that I hadn't yet had time to go through them. I dropped them on the breakfast table and resolved to do so over a cup of tea. Then I heard a 'Pack-pack-paaaaarck' noise just outside my side door, and I don't know about you, but whenever I hear a 'Pack-pack-Paaaaarck' noise, I have to investigate. I opened said door, and was confronted by a large, brown chicken. Now forgive my ignorance, but I always get confused about the correct name for these creatures, so it may well have been a hen, a cockerel, a rooster, or a bantam fowl. Whatever it was, it was certainly noisy. I instantly realized that this was a lay-by bird; in Wales they're usually chaffinches – creatures that become tame after being fed on a regular basis by every motor home driver that ever took a breather en route to somewhere else. And this one was demanding food NOW. You could tell by the way it was shrieking at me and stamping its foot. I went back into the van and found a biscuit, which I crumbled up and threw to it. This seemed to do the trick. Then, as mysteriously as it had arrived, the thing strutted off down a narrow path and disappeared. Bemused, I followed it, just as Alice followed the white rabbit, to see where it was going. Very soon, the path entered a lush rainforest area, with dense foliage and exotic palms – all very different to what I had seen on South Island. The path had now become completely overgrown and the stroppy chicken was nowhere to be seen, so I turned around and walked back along the path to where my motor home was parked, and I use the word 'was' advisedly.

My Kore-Take motor home wasn't there any more.

Have you ever had something stolen? It's a very disconcerting experience, I can tell you. You think of a dozen possible scenarios before it dawns on you that person or persons unknown have taken the thing. You wonder if you have somehow strayed onto another pathway that brings you out a hundred yards further down the road. You ask yourself if you actually arrived in a motor home in the first place, or if you were just confusing it with something you did the week before. You imagine that you left the handbrake off, and your holiday home is now in the ocean at the bottom of the mountain you were driving over. After several, even more improbable scenarios, it finally dawns on you. Some shit bag has nicked it. Then an awful, gut-wrenching feeling of nausea engulfs you, as you begin to realize the multiple implications of someone's vile, selfish act. Mr Maori was on board, for starters – my *raison d'être* and meal ticket. My camcorder with the footage of the sperm whale and the dolphins, my brand-new digital Nikon full of memories, my clothes, Uncle Ken's letters, my cornflakes, all those teabags, my passport, my wallet.

No, I had my wallet in my trousers. This was a start, but not much of one. Then there was the motor home itself, for Christ's sake. That was probably a cool fifty grand's worth on its own, and here I was worrying about cameras. I'd be crucified by the insurance company. I'd only gone and left the bloody keys in the ignition. How dim was that, on a scale of one to tin? For the best part of an hour, I just sat there, with nothing going on in my head at all. The chicken turned up again and pecked my leg, so I told it to fuck off. It was his fault, the little bastard. Maybe he was in league with them, whoever they were.

Then the mists cleared, and I realized that I was miles from anywhere and I needed help. I stood at the edge of the lay-by and thumbed for a lift, and within half an hour, a huge articulated lorry pulled up and the driver invited me on board. Having quickly checked to make sure he wasn't wearing a black leather peaked cap, lederhosen and a big bushy moustache, I jumped in, explained my predicament, and he offered his sympathy. He explained that New Zealand was a wonderful place, but even in wonderful places there were scumbags; usually crystal meth addicts – whatever that is – who steal anything that's not nailed down in order to fund their vile habit. It was then that I began to suspect the carload of roughnecks that I'd passed at the previous lay-by; three lads with hoodies in a beaten up Ford. My saviour said he was heading for Wanganui, as I had been, and could drop me there. It was, as I suspected, a big place, where I could find a bed and breakfast, contact the police, and eat. I thanked him profusely. Half an hour later, we drove through a dusty, one-horse town that was called something like Rikkitikkitavi.

Then I saw it.

There, next to a café on an unmade gravel car park, was my motor home.

I screamed for the driver to stop, and thanked him profusely for his help. He asked if I'd be okay, and begged me not to get involved or do anything foolish. (I noticed he hadn't volunteered to help me.) I assured him that I was not the hero type, and leapt down from the lorry. I tip-toed across to the café and took a look around. My motor home was locked up. Quite ironic that, if you think about it. The thieves were being more careful with my possessions than I was. I peered inside, and everything seemed to be as I'd left it. There was a battered red Ford Fiesta next to it, full of dog-ends. It looked as if my theory about the perpetrators was bang on. Then I took a surreptitious peek into the café window, and it was confirmed. The three youths were ordering food from the counter, which was good news. It meant that they weren't going to be leaving for at least ten minutes.

As I paced the ground, desperately trying to formulate a plan that didn't involve my premature and violent death, a rather swanky Ferrari Testarossa growled onto the car park. The owner and his lady friend got out, and had a brief discussion about where they would eat, which revealed to me that they were Americans by birth. They both quickly agreed that the run-down café was not to their liking, but they seemed taken with the swanky fish restaurant over the road and fifty yards down, so they decided on that.

'What about moving the car down there?' asked the lady, who, being American, didn't like to walk anywhere as it made her appear less rich.

'Ah, come on, Hun,' pleaded the husband. 'Let's get into the spirit. We don't live in Dallas any more. We need to live like the locals do. It's a nice day. We'll take a stroll.'

The lady gave him a withering look, and tottered off in her high heels, closely followed by J.R. Ewing.

I glanced over at their beautiful vehicle, and noticed that they'd left the window open and the keys in the ignition. After what had happened to me, I couldn't allow this couple to have their Ferrari stolen by the three stooges in the café. I was about to call after them, when all of a sudden, an idea hit me like a bolt of lightning. As I looked across the High Street at the Americans, I noticed a charity shop. In fact, I noticed several. New Zealand, like England, seemed to be littered with them, but the one that interested me had a man's black suit in the window. I crossed the road, entered the shop, and examined the suit.

'Kin oi hilp you?' asked the lady assistant, recoiling slightly from the persistent pungency of my perfume.

'Er, yes,' I replied. 'I need a cheap black suit, for, erm, a funeral. I'm on holiday, and all I have is shorts and T-shirts. How much is it?'

'Twinty dollars,' she smiled. 'It'll fit you too, by the looks of it. 'Do you want to try it on?'

'Yes please!' I said, grabbing the clothing and dashing into her tiny changing room. My heart was pounding now, and my mouth was dry. The suit was a perfect fit. I exited the room still wearing it, paid the lady with trembling hand and dashed out of the shop. I walked twenty yards down the street, so that the hoodies couldn't see me, crossed the road to the car park, reached into the breast pocket of my shirt and popped on my free-with-the-toothpaste Ray Bans. I glanced around to make sure J.R. and Sue Ellen were still enjoying their Blue Cod, and then jumped into the driving seat of their Ferrari. I started the mighty engine and pulled the car round to the front window of the café, revving for all I was worth and praying that the Yanks didn't recognize that distinctive roar from across the road. To my delight, the three stooges ran over to the window to take a look. I got out of the car, locked the door, flicked open my mobile phone and strode into the café.

I walked up to the counter, trying my best to look as Nicholas Cage-like as was humanly possible, and ordered 'Uno cappuccino, per favore.' The waitress gave me a strange look, probably induced by the accent or the aftershave, or both, but understood what I was after. She handed me the drink, I paid, and then sat down as close to the three stooges as I could. They were now staring at me as if I'd arrived from another planet. I had. I was from Sicily.

Now, I'm one of those people for whom foreign languages are a closed book, but for some reason, I seem to have a knack with the accents. In other words, I may only know eighteen words of Italian, but boy, can I pronounce them properly, and with gusto. I am a bit of a Mynah bird, and I hear how it's said and am able to mimic it. I continued my bogus phone conversation, in hushed, gravelly tones, making sure the boys heard every word.

'Ah, ciao, Don Caleffi. Come stai? Molto bene. Si, si, grazie.'

It was around there that my grasp of Italian disintegrated, so I decided that the Don and I should continue in English.

'Scusa, Don Caleffi. Inglesi, per favore.' And then, in an accent perfected by Chico Marx, 'The people who steala your motor home don't know who they deal with, Don Caleffi. Yes, capito. I understand, but theese is notta Sicily, Don Caleffi. I can't keel people here, like I do for you at home. Maybe you should just call the carabinieri......okay, okay, I understand. They musta be taken out. Eeef that issa your wish, Don Caleffi. Si, si, I have it here.'

I tapped the inside pocket of my cheap suit, to where my imaginary Beretta was situated. The three stooges were now staring at me, transfixed. I reciprocated with the coldest, meanest stare I could muster, continuing to rub my pocket as I did so. One of the lads tapped the other, and whispered something in his ear. The third one appeared to be in some private hell, and had developed an unhealthy, clammy look. Suddenly, they made a beeline for the door. I walked over to the window to observe their movements, but I was interrupted by the waitress.

'Excuse me. Have those characters gone yit? Only they lift their bunch of keys on the table.'

'Non problemo!' I assured her. 'I willa take the keys forra them.'

I left the café, just as the red Fiesta screeched off the car park in a cloud of dust and hit the highway. I pocketed my van keys and strolled across the road to the Ocean Restaurant. J.R. and Sue Ellen were in the window seat, halfway through a messy lobster.

'Excuse me,' I said, handing the Ferrari keys to J.R. 'You left these in your sports car with the window open, so I've locked it for you. You can't be too careful you know!'

'Gee, thanks!' he replied, wiping his chin with a napkin. 'Very civil of you, but there was no need to worry. Unlike England and the States, you can leave your cars open all day here, and no one steals them.'

'Is that right?' I asked. 'I'm new here, so I didn't realize.'

'Absolutely,' he assured me, 'and before you go, I hope you don't mind me pointing it out, my friend, but your suit still has the twenty dollar price tag on it, just there on the arm.'

CHIPTAH 14

In which I am joined on my journey by a new friend, and experience a JFK moment.

Lake Taupo is the largest lake in New Zealand, and the area plays host to thousands of mad adventurers who prefer leaping from mountains attached to rubber bands to colonic irrigation, though both produce the same results. Personally, I'd had my fair share of excitement, what with one thing and another, so I was happy to find the Top Tin and have a well-earned rest.

Originally, I'd planned to visit Rotorua at the very end of my stay, before driving back to the airport in Auckland, but after my various disasters I was feeling nervous and didn't want to risk losing Mr Maori again. Consequently, after consulting my expensive map over a cup of tea, I decided to head west to see a few attractions that had been recommended to me, and then proceed to Rotorua as soon as possible afterwards in order to get the business part of the trip over with. I could head north to the Bay of Islands afterwards – having absolved myself of all responsibilities – and just unwind. I was just plotting my exact route, when I heard a quacking sound at my side door. Naturally, I opened it, and was confronted by not one, not two, but fifteen Mallard ducks of both sexes. This was getting a bit rich. Were they part of an international gang of motor home thieves, or was every single bird on these islands trained to GCSE level in how to extricate food from holiday makers? Did any of the buggers still remember how to hunt for worms, I wondered, or did they feel that that was now beneath them?

I glanced across towards the site office and noticed a large white sign instructing campers not to feed the ducks, so, being an upstanding citizen, I didn't. I closed the door, and the quacking started in earnest once more. I opened the door again and asked them to clear off, but a fat lot of good that did. Then I made a shooing gesture and this did the trick, but one male duck still stood there stubbornly, quacking away and staring at me with an imploring look. I threw it a bit of stale toast, which it gobbled up immediately. Then it quacked again, so I threw some more. I pointed out the sign on the office wall to him, but he didn't seem at all concerned about it. I shut the door, after promising I'd give him a bit more at breakfast the following day if he'd clear off immediately and leave me in peace. Strangely, this he did. Either this duck understood English, or else it was just a coincidence. My money was on the latter, but having owned a psychic dog for six years, I could no longer be sure of anything.

The following morning, my friendly duckwas there again, so I gave him some more toast, before heading over to the shower block to freshen up.

Invigorated after a three-token shower, I set off around ten o'clock, itching like mad to see the sights; though I think the mosquitoes may have had a hand in it too – the itching I mean. After a quick skim around the bottom half of the lake, which was, as ever, predictably scenic, I made a brief excursion into town to buy one of those black polo shirts with the New Zealand logo and fern motif – the one that all the tourists buy. I then left Turangi and joined Motorway 41 heading towards Taumarunui. I wanted to see the Waitomo Glow Worm Caves, the Angora Rabbit Shearing Shed, Te-Awamutu and the Kiwi Sanctuary, all for very different reasons. I was tootling along, smiling to myself at the previous day's adventure and feeling extremely grateful to get my van back intact, when a massive great juggernaut that was driving right up my arse, honked his horn at me and scared me out of my wits. This was his gentle and caring way of suggesting that I stop hogging the middle lane, and let him do it instead. I took a peek at my rear-view mirror, flashed him a two-fingered sign by way of admitting that I was in lane two when I shouldn't have been, mouthed a choice expletive, and pulled over. He sailed past and proffered his erect middle finger, by way of telling me, presumably, that lane one was where I belonged, to which I reacted by smiling my sickliest smile, just to annoy him. Then a thought flashed across my mind so quickly that it didn't give me time to catch hold of it, but it left me feeling curiously edgy all the same. Something wasn't right, but I couldn't think what it was. Suddenly the thought broke cover and quickly darted across my mind again, zigzagging this way and that, like a startled antelope being pursued by a cheetah. This time, however, I managed to catch a clear glimpse of it, and realized what had been subconsciously troubling me. I looked into my rear-view mirror again. It hadn't been a trick of the light after all, or a hallucination, caused by the stress of dealing with road hogs.

There was a Mallard duck sitting on the back seat of my motor home.

I pulled into the nearest rest area I could find, parked up and went to investigate. The duck, it has to be said, seemed pleased to see me. My mind was reeling now, as I tried to imagine how the thing could possibly have sneaked on board. Then it dawned on me. I had left the side door pinned back on the latch when I went for my shower. It *would* be easy to criticize, after I managed to get the van stolen the day before, but this was on a Top Tin camp site, not a country lay-by, and everyone did it. The duck had obviously wandered in, searching for toast, and finding none, had settled into a comfy settee and taken a nap. I fetched it a saucer of water and some bread, which it demolished with relish, and then – and I swear this is true – it sat on my lap, like Len always does. I felt quite paternal at this point, and gently stroked the thing, an action it did nothing to rebuff. My big problem was, I was too far away to return to Turangi, but I was worried that it would miss its family and friends. I would have to turf it out at some other town, where it wouldn't know anyone, and this seemed cruel. I'd have adopted the thing, but I was flying home in a fortnight, and ducks weren't allowed in the hand luggage. I have to admit that the very thought of this made me smile, because it reminded me of all those old books you used to find in the library as a kid, written by the likes of Gerald Durrell, with titles like 'A Capybara in my Suitcase'.

Taking the duck home clearly wasn't an option, but I felt that evicting the thing onto the nearest bit of grass wasn't either. That 'out of sight, out of mind' attitude is all very well, but I couldn't live with myself if it got squashed by the likes of that bastard in the juggernaut. Possums were one thing, but Mallard ducks were altogether another kettle of fish, I felt. And this raised another important point. It seemed rude to keep calling the little fellow 'the duck', or 'it'. I felt he needed a name, especially if we were to be travelling companions until I could find him a new home. I grabbed the pen and notepad, and tried to come up with a few suggestions, while the duck looked on.

My first idea was Chris Piddock, which I quite liked, even though it was a bit sick. Come on, catch up – I haven't got all day. Crispy duck; Chinese delicacy. This was quickly followed by Bill Platypus, as in Duck Bill Platypus of course. After a further ten minutes of wracking my brains I couldn't think of any better ones, so I tossed a dollar and my first attempt won it. I lifted Chris gently off my lap and returned to the driver's seat, eager to reach Rotorua as quickly as possible. After a couple of miles he'd tucked his head into his back in that peculiar way ducks do, and dozed off, so I stopped worrying about him and concentrated on my driving.

The New Zealanders have a rather robust, and at the same time, pleasingly, humorous attitude to road safety. In England, the motorway information signs occasionally ask us in that earnest, po-faced way of theirs, not to drink and drive, to slow down, take a break, and stop using mobile phones. In New Zealand, however, you are more likely to come across ad agency-designed shock posters, with messages like, 'Carry on driving like that, you cretin, and you'll end up on a mortuary slab', or 'People who drink eight pints and drive home often end up being given another eight pints – of blood'. Okay, I admit I invented those two, but the real ones are, if anything, even worse. There was one that I passed on the South Island that warned of the dangers of driving whilst tired, the gist of which was, if you fall asleep at the wheel, you tend not to wake up ever again. Strangely, I was wide awake until I started reading these roadside signs, and all of a sudden I began to feel drowsy, which seemed to defeat the object of having them in a way – maybe there was a touch of auto-suggestion going on. Anyway, my golden rule is: it's time to take a break when you have to resort to licking your fingers and wetting your eyelids in order to stay awake. Another good indication that you're over-tired is not remembering a thing about driving through Pungapunga. (Come to think of it, I should imagine that nearly everyone in the world can't remember driving through it, but that's probably because they never have. I, on the other hand, actually did, but I can't, if you follow me.) The best one, though, is when you literally can't keep your eyes open any longer. You begin to do slow blinks, and the time you allow them to stay closed just gets longer and longer until your head sinks to your chest, and suddenly it lurches back bolt upright, just in time for you to correct the steering and prevent your motor home from plunging into an abyss. This was what happened to me on the way to Taumarunui, and the only thing that saved my life was the assassination attempt.

Mesmerised by the long and winding road, just as my old friend McCartney had been, I must have nodded off for a few seconds, when all of a sudden there was a mighty crack, which woke me with a start. I also recall emitting a blood-curdling scream. There was a perfect, round bullet hole in my windscreen, and had the bullet actually entered the cabin instead of bouncing off the toughened glass, I would also have had a nice neat hole in the middle of my brow, which would have meant curtains, and I don't mean nice, floral Laura Ashley ones. It's bad enough for the nerves when someone suddenly shakes you while you're dozing in the old armchair, so that they can hand you a cup of tea, but when you're rudely awoken by what, to all intents and purposes, seems like an attempt on your life with a 22 calibre sniper rifle, it's a good ten minutes before you can breathe properly again. That said, it was infinitely preferable to ploughing over a cliff, which would almost certainly have happened, had the bullet not hit the screen first. I screeched to a halt, and skittishly scanned the terrain for the three hoodies. The only explanation I could come up with was that they had spotted me, taken exception to my bogus Mafia hit man routine, and exacted their revenge. The coast appeared to be clear, so I opened the cabin door a few inches, looking for signs of movement in the roadside ferns. I saw nothing. The sniper had probably fired his gun from a car coming in the opposite direction, and was now long gone. I examined the hole. It was perfectly circular and around three-eighths of an inch in diameter. Luckily, it had only pierced the first half of the laminated screen and, miraculously, not caused the whole thing to cave in and shatter into a million pieces. As I stood examining the damage, another motor home came belting around the bend, just as another bullet hit my screen, inches from my head. I dived to the floor, commando-style, and tried to roll under the van to protect myself; a manoeuvre I'd seen the likes of Tom Cruise pull off on many occasions. It was then that I noticed the road sign, warning of loose chippings, and the feet of the motor home driver strolling across to apologize for adding another hole to my windscreen.

'Are you okay?' he asked. 'Did one of them hit you? I'm dreadfully sorry!'

Well, I felt a complete fool, I can tell you. I creaked to my feet and dusted myself off. I had pieces of gravel embedded into my brow from the freshly-made road, and a pair of matching grazed knees. The driver carefully removed a cigarette butt from my cheek, and began to dust me down with his handkerchief. I thanked him for his concern, made my excuses, and decided that what I needed more than anything was a lie down. The man apologized some more, and was about to return to his family, when he turned and added:

'I hope you don't mind my mentioning this, but there appears to be an agitated-looking Mallard duck on your dashboard.'

'I know,' I replied. 'His name is Chris.'

Feeling that I had clarified things for him, and that I could add nothing further to the conversation, I jumped back into the cab and headed for the nearest lay-by to calm down.

I decided that it was probably best to rest a while following my near-death experience, but I couldn't seem to drift off, partly due to Chris wanting to lie on my face, and partly due to my mosquito bites, which had all decided to start itching at the same time. I seemed to have collected around three hundred mosquito bites after my stay at the lake, and they were beginning to get on my nerves. For some reason, I have always been a mosquito magnet. They will often completely ignore the person next to me, but feast on me till the cows come home, and even after that sometimes. Silly as it sounds, I actually believe they are drawing on me. After Taupo, my body resembled a giant join-the-dots picture, and I'm sure they were actually working on a facsimile of Van Gogh's sunflowers, having examined their handiwork in the mirror. To take my mind off the itching I began to peruse my guide book, after I'd persuaded Chris to settle next to me. I read a chapter about Captain Cook, and learned that after discovering New Zealand, he was eaten by Hawaiians. They kept that quiet in the school history books. The Maoris were also originally cannibals, according to my guide, which made me feel a bit nervous about going to Rotorua, if I'm honest. It's interesting, isn't it, how England is asked to apologize for all sorts of things it has supposedly inflicted on people, such as the slave trade and colonising half of the world against its will, not to mention Noel Edmonds and Tony Blackburn, and yet no one has yet thought to ask Hawaii to apologize for eating our Captain Cook. I made a mental note to write to Parliament on my return, and demand that Jack Johnson should pen a musical apology on behalf of his country. He could compose something that sounds like all the other songs he writes, but with different lyrics – a bit like Elton John did when Princess Diana died. I began doodling on my notebook and came up with this. (You have to imagine it being sung by Jack, with scantily clad Polynesian women wearing garlands around their necks dancing seductively and adding the backing vocals.)

We shouldn'ta killed Cook

Aloha Hoy!

We shouldn'ta cooked Cook

Aloha Hoy!

Ready steady Cook

Aloha Hoy!

Chorus: *What shall we have him with?*

Chips, chips!

We deserve indigestion

Who scoffed his lips?

Who got da butt?

Me did, me did!

Who got da knob?

Me did, me did!

Who got da nose?

Me did, me did!

Put some salad in his hat!

Well, I didn't say it was any good, did I? Remember, I'd just had a nasty shock, and I was brain-dead from all that driving, so I probably wasn't as sharp mentally as I'd have liked. The whole thing about cannibalism did fascinate me though. I wondered if Captain Cook tasted like chicken. Every other unusual type of meat that anyone's ever tried does, apparently.

As a consequence of this gruesome discovery, I decided to offer my own, simple, heartfelt tribute to the great explorer by christening my motor home Endeavour 2. After all, I felt as if I were following in Cook's footsteps myself, and having almost as many wild adventures. I even thought about keeping a captain's log, like they do on Star Trek. You know the kind of thing:

Monday

I have had no female company for days. Even Chris is beginning to look attractive. I may stop off in town to buy him a lipstick for his beak. No, stop! What am I saying? He's a male duck. I may be weird, but I'm not yet gay. Ask me again next week.

Tuesday

Ten days without food or water. All of a sudden I am beginning to see Chris in yet another light. Unless I can find a road-kill possum. I wonder if ducks like the taste of possum. I wonder if I will, come to think of it. Hopefully, it will taste just like chicken.

Wednesday

Managed to find enough bread and water to feed Chris at least. He seems to love it, which is odd, because it's a meal often regarded as a punishment for prisoners. I wonder what naughty ducks are given to eat in jail. Fillet steak maybe?

Thursday

Made Chris walk the plank today. I know he was planning a mutiny. Also, we had strawberries in the fridge, which I picked

179

from a roadside bush, and some cream which I got from a roadside cow, and I know he helped himself to two portions. And my Bounty bar is missing.

Friday

I think I'm getting delirious. Chris is back and he keeps mocking me, with that horrible, sarcastic laugh of his.

However, after much thought, I shelved the idea. I *was* feeling a little delirious though, joking aside, and I wasn't sure if it was due to spending too much time either on my own, or with just a duck for company, neither of which encouraged witty banter and the flow of soul, or whatever the expression is. My mind seemed to be flitting from one obscure subject to another, and lacked focus. For example, one of the things that was exercising me was the one-armed man situation. I couldn't recall when I'd last seen one in England, other than on top of Nelson's Column, but they were everywhere Down Under. I had seen one in a large clothing shop in Wellington, and there was another at the petrol station-cum-hardware store in Turanga. As if this wasn't enough, I saw another one-armed chap on a whale-watching trip, and to deepen the mystery, all three had their *left* arm missing. Was this as a result of a tropical disease that only manifested itself in New Zealand, or had they all been victims of shark attacks, proffering their left arms so that if they happened to survive, they could still write home from the intensive care ward? Perhaps, they were all clumsy combine harvester drivers, or maybe band saw operators with poor eyesight. I vowed to research this on the internet upon my return.

God, I was restless. I flicked through a copy of a local newspaper, but it offered little in the way of distraction. In the medical section, a woman had been given a new nipple, which the doctor had fashioned from her ear lobe. This prompted several questions. Firstly, what happened to her old nipple in the first place? Did it simply drop off one day? Secondly, did she value her nipples more than her ears, because now she had a new nipple, but

180

the bottom of her ear was missing. Surely, unless she went around naked all the time, no one would have noticed her missing nipple – except perhaps her newborn child – but a chunk out of her ear would have been as obvious as a tarantula on a slice of angel cake. There was also a strange article about an American writer called Joan Brady who had won the Whitbread prize, but fifteen years after she had hit the literary limelight, she was reduced to penning cheapo crime stories, and was in dire straits financially. Apparently, she was suing the nearby shoe-repair workshop. Yes, I had to read that bit twice too. She reckoned that the fumes from their glue had addled her mind, and was claiming one hundred and fifteen thousand pounds in compensation. And do you know what? She got it. That's America for you. Perhaps I could claim a similar amount for the fumes coming from my pet duck, which had reduced me to writing absolute bilge.

I remembered that I still hadn't read any of Ken's old letters, and they promised to be far more entertaining than the local newspaper, given his track record. The trouble was, it was getting late, and I didn't fancy a night in a lay-by after my earlier trauma, so once more, I deferred reading them until the following day. That was the thing about New Zealand, I found; the pace of life was so much slower than back home. I started up the engine and was about to pull away, when my phone rang. It was Fu Manchu, with good news. He was good at keeping me up to speed, I'll say that much. Two hoodlums had been arrested as a result of my plan, and had pleaded guilty after a few hours in a dark room with Fu and the boys. He more or less told me that I had redeemed myself for my earlier stupidity, and he was willing to let sleeping dogs lie. I can't tell you how delighted I was about this. It fair perked me up, I can tell you. He asked me to pass on his regards to Tina and Jake in England when I next phoned home, as, between us, we had closed down a very successful smuggling operation and taken two very nasty Singaporean scumbags out of circulation for a *very* long time. Knowing Singapore as I now did, that probably meant forever, and then some. He bade me farewell, and even

181

offered to buy me a beer on the way home, if he wasn't busy. The man was almost human after all!

It was then, with renewed vigour, that I set off for Te Kuiti to check out the Waitomo caves, after insisting that Chris went outside for a toilet break. I half expected the little fellow to waddle off into the long grass and disappear, but no. As soon as he'd done his business, he hopped up the steps and settled back inside again. I was already dreading our farewells in a couple of weeks' time. It was surely going to break his little heart. (And mine.) I'd heard about these ducks that pop out of the egg and attach themselves to the first person they see, thinking it's their mother. I realized that I hadn't known him since birth, but that kind of unbreakable bond was pretty much how it was beginning to be with Chris and me. I was surely going to have to trick him into going outside for a pee on our last day together in Auckland, and then drive off sharpish – something I was already feeling incredibly guilty and disheartened about doing, but I knew I didn't really have another option.

The Top Tin was conveniently situated immediately opposite the caves. I purchased a ticket and then tried in vain to introduce Chris to the posse of ducks that had assembled outside my door in search of food. He waddled over to take a peek at them, and I swear his quacking took on a disdainful tone, as if he disapproved of their antics, now that he part-owned his own motor home. It was almost as if he'd forgotten his roots. As he stood, looking down on his own kind from the lofty heights of the second step, I admit that I gave him a gentle kick up the arse, hoping he'd fall down the steps into their midst and get a feel for street life again. Instead, he just gave me a withering look, which almost tempted me to rename him Bill Withers.

I grabbed my fleece, left Chris on the settee with an assurance that I'd be back later, and headed out to the caves. My mate, who is a tree surgeon (not that this has any bearing whatsoever on the story), had told me all about the Glow Worm Caves, and the Angora Rabbit Shearing Shed nearby. Ordinarily, anyone who recommended such odd-ball tourist attractions would have

182

eceived the contempt they deserved, but I did trust his judgement, nd he assured me that I would not be disappointed. And lisappointed I was not. We were ferried through the caves by oat, and asked to look above us, where thousands and thousands of little glow worms lit up the cathedral-like ceiling, resembling hose tiny, sequenced fairy lights that people decorate their Christmas trees with. It was all quite beautiful, I have to say, and he Angora rabbit place was going to have to go some to beat it. An hour and a half later, I was pulling onto its dusty car park, not nowing what to expect, but wondering how on earth anyone in heir right mind could include the place on any 'must see' tinerary. It had all the hallmarks of Paperweight World (an unbelievably mind-numbingly boring tourist attraction back in the JK), as far as I was concerned. I walked in and was met by a riendly middle-aged lady who showed me shelves full of wool, nd I remember thinking that Keith Moon wouldn't have cared a ot for the place. That primal adrenalin rush thing that New Zealanders seemed to go for just wasn't in evidence. I was eginning to think my tree surgeon had been inhaling too much ap and it had sent him barking. Then the lady's colleague arrived vith a huge rabbit that resembled a white fluffy beach ball with yes. I'd never seen anything like it, and neither had the coach-oad of Japanese tourists that had just walked in. We formed a emi-circle around what looked to be a medieval torture table, vhilst the lady, who had now clipped on a radio-mike, explained hat she was about to relieve Priscilla – for that was the rabbit's ame – of its Angora wool. Scores of cameras clicked as Priscilla's legs were fitted, one by one, into restraining straps. Heather, our hostess, explained that this didn't hurt the creature nd that Angora rabbits had to be regularly sheared or they would ecome most uncomfortable, and even die of overheating. This truck me as strange, because, unless God created shearing sheds t the same time that he created the Angora rabbit, surely they vould not have been equipped to survive. Maybe they simply lidn't, and after He had spotted His design flaw, He quickly nvented shearing sheds to make amends. I am still puzzled as to why He didn't just redesign the rabbit though, if I am honest, but I suppose He was creating employment, which is a good thing. Anyway, the thing was now in its stirrups, looking relaxed and blasé, like it had done this many times before. Heather then wound a crank of sorts, which appeared to stretch the rabbit by around a foot. I was reminded of nothing so much as the rack, but whereas the rack was employed when a sadistic jailer needed to know, for example, who had helped Guido Fawkes to carry the barrels into the vaults, this device seemed to cause no ill-effects whatsoever. The exact same manoeuvre would have induced blood-curdling screams from the gunpowder plotters, but the rabbit just affected an air of nonchalance, sniffing occasionally with its cute pink nose. Still Heather applied the screw, and now the poor thing was at least five feet long, but the rabbit appeared unperturbed, save for maybe a hint of world-weary resignedness.

Satisfied that her victim was now more than three times its original length, Heather plugged in her clippers, again, to the backdrop of a blitz of camera shutters. (No flashguns were allowed as they frightened the rabbits. Apparently, being stretched was okay, but Angoras were camera-shy.) Then, to my amazement and delight, she began to rotate the rabbit, as if it were on a spit, by turning a handle with her other hand and clipping away as she did so. Meanwhile, Priscilla just took it without a complaint. I'm sure, if she had had access to a magazine, she would have passed the time by reading it, and I was half-expecting Heather to engage her in conversation about her forthcoming package holiday.

I don't think I have laughed so much in years. You had to be there. I offered a silent apology to my tree surgeon friend, for ever doubting him. It was delightful, and priceless, and such was the overwhelming feeling of benevolence I now had for the place, I purchased a quantity of wool for my mother to knit a jumper with, even though I knew it would be like pearls before swine. The last thing she knitted for me was a balaclava, when I was at infants' school, but it would have made a far better jumper.

The following day, after Chris and I had made up, we filled the van's water tank, emptied the chemical lavatory and drove to Otorohanga, where the Kiwi house was situated. I say 'made up', because when I got back from my dinner, over the road at the Caves Restaurant, he seemed a bit shirty with me, and all the explaining about the restaurant's no ducks policy and my offer of a quick game of three card brag did nothing to lighten his mood. He just shuffled up the far end of the settee and sulked, while I drank the last of my bottle of Shiraz. You could have cut the bloody atmosphere with a knife, I'm not kidding. Thankfully, a good night's sleep seemed to have restored his bonhomie, so we were away on our next adventure, and this time he was able to accompany me. I was heading towards Te-Awamutu for soppy, sentimental reasons which I will explain in the fullness of time, but I couldn't resist spending an hour at the Kiwi house en route, because I'd never seen one, and it was, after all, the national bird of New Zealand. I did have an ulterior motive too, if I am honest. The Kiwi house is in the middle of a wildfowl centre, with lakes and pretty tropical gardens, and I wanted Chris to take a walk around with me, in the hope that he'd like the place, maybe meet a woman, and settle down there. I paid the man in the kiosk and sidled in with my pet duck waddling in behind me. If the chap saw him, he never said anything. I suppose ducks just wandered hither and thither anyway, so it wouldn't have looked untoward. We mooched around the ponds for a while, and I pointed out the female ducks that I thought he might take a shine to, adding comments such as, 'Look Chris, see that one over there on that rock. She fancies you. Look how she keeps looking at you. Go and ask her for her phone number, why don't you?' Chris, however, only had eyes for me. I was beginning to suspect that if he ever came back in the next life as a human, he would be a British Airways cabin steward. It was surely just a matter of time before he asked me to put some blond streaks in his turquoise hairdo and gel it up for him. We reached the Kiwi house, and this was where I intended to instigate my cunning plan. I told Chris to hang around outside while I took a peek at the Kiwis, which are shy, nocturnal creatures. Their house is fitted with extremely subdued lighting, which encourages them to put in the odd appearance during the day for the sake of the Japanese tourists. No other wildfowl are allowed in, unless of course they have a valid ticket, so I intended to sneak off for half an hour, by which time, hopefully, the call of nature would have done its bit and I would return to find Chris snogging with a hot female under the shade of a palm tree. A bit like in *The Jungle Book*, when Mowgli meets that foxy chick filling up her pitcher at the water's edge.

Ignoring his squawks, I strode into the Kiwi house without looking back, though it pained me to do so. The interior consisted of a narrow walkway for the visitors, and a large room made to look like a section of rainforest at night, with tree trunks, ferns, pathways and so on. There was everything except Kiwis, in fact. I stood there like a lemon, with three Japanese folks, waiting to glimpse a bit of Kiwi action, but none came. The Japs were especially pissed off because there were signs everywhere telling them that on no account could they take pictures, as the flashes freaked the birds out. The look on their faces said it all. It was as if their raison d'être had been whisked away from them. For the first time in their lives, they would have to experience something and not record it for posterity. That's if the Kiwis ever condescended to make an appearance of course.

Then, just as I was about to give up and go back outside to see how Chris was getting on, I noticed a stirring in the undergrowth, and eventually, not one, but two Kiwis appeared, and I have to report that they are odd creatures. They were both around a foot and a half tall, chocolate brown in colour, with long pointed beaks. The first one seemed very interested in a tree trunk (I suppose you have to make your own entertainment if there's no telly) and he began to poke his beak into a large knothole in the bark. He stayed in this position – eventually becoming totally motionless – for ages, with his big fat backside sticking out for us tourists to look at. The second one just kept waddling up and down the faux-woodland path with a distracted air, as if bored senseless (which it

186

probably was). After treading the exact same route, back and forth, back and forth, until he'd worn a groove in the floor, the Kiwi headed towards the tree trunk – where his inanimate colleague was still contemplating the meaning of life with its bottom stuck out and its beak in a knothole – but his stride now seemed to indicate a strong sense of purpose. Having reached his intended destination, he suddenly gave the other bird a vicious peck up the arse, which looked to me like the culmination of years of pent-up frustration and anger coming to the boil. This must have come as a considerable shock to the one with its beak in the knothole, judging by the almighty screech it emitted. It backed out with some urgency, unsheathing its beak from the tree, and having ascertained the identity of its assailant – not a difficult task when there were only two of them in the first place – it charged, pecking chunks out of the other bird whilst chasing it down the woodland path, back into the hole in the wall that presumably led to their sleeping quarters. Further screeches ensued from within before silence resumed, and the show, for the time being, was over. It was the nearest thing I have ever seen to Tweedledum and Tweedledee, and, after an unpromising start, worth every penny of the entry fee. I waved goodbye to the Japanese, who preferred to hang around just in case round two kicked off, and strode outside into the warm sunshine to find Chris. This didn't take me long, as he was hanging around the turnstiles with a disgruntled look. When he saw me, he went ballistic, quacking and flapping around. As I bent down to try to pacify him, he jumped into my arms, as would a tame kitten, much to the amazement of passers-by. I picked him up, stroked his little turquoise head, and made for the exit.

It was then that the trouble started.

A man dressed in khaki from the ticket kiosk called to me as Chris and I were heading across the car park to the Endeavour. Not realizing he was shouting after me I carried on walking, so he left his post and gave chase.

187

'Where on earth do you think you're going with that duck?' he shouted.

'Te Awamutu,' I replied, helpfully. On the surface, I tried to remain calm, but all of a sudden I could see where this was going.

'I don't think so!' he snarled. 'Put it down please, or I'll call security.'

'Oh, oh yes, I see!' I began falteringly. 'No, the thing is, this isn't one of your ducks...'

'Put the duck down, please.'

'Let me explain,' I begged, my heart pounding now. 'I arrived here with this duck. It's a pet duck, and now we're leaving. I haven't stolen it!'

'That's one of our ducks, sir, and you must put it down now or you'll be arrested.'

'How on earth do you know that it's one of your ducks?' I demanded. 'They all look the bloody same. Anyway, you saw me arrive with it.'

'Don't be ridiculous, sir,' replied the man, who seemed to be getting very hot under the collar now. 'I did no such thing. Put the duck down NOW!'

I don't know about you, but when there's a principle at stake, I tend to get a little stubborn. I ignored his rantings, and headed for the Endeavour.

This, in hindsight, was probably a mistake.

CHIPTAH 15

In which I travel to Te Awamutu, looking for Finns.

Otorohanga police station looked to be no more than two small rooms. I don't suppose they needed more in a place that quiet. There'd be the odd drunk of a weekend, a few badly parked vehicles to tow away, the occasional convenience store theft, and that was about it. Oh yes, and the English duck thief – the chap who would make the front page of the *Otorohanga Times*, thanks to his outrageous crime of the century. Someone had already tipped off *the* journalist – note that I didn't say *a* journalist – and he was in the other room, waiting to get his scoop. Meanwhile, I was getting a grilling from a chap who fancied himself as Tommy Lee Jones, of *No Country for Old Men* fame. I was in the middle of explaining my side of the story for the tenth time when a young rookie cop burst in, like Pheidippides bringing news of victory from the battle of Marathon. Well, it wasn't *quite* that dramatic, because the Greek bloke had to run twenty-six miles after fighting a battle in forty degree heat wearing full armour, whereas this young copper had driven three miles in his air-conditioned cop car, but that aside, he did seem as if he urgently wanted to convey something of great pith and moment to his craggy superior. Instead, he was waved down and told not to interrupt his boss in mid-flow.

'This duck,' continued Tommy Lee slowly, stroking his chin.

'Chris,' I added helpfully.

'Chris. You reckon it adopted you near Taupo.'

'Yis. Sorry, I mean yes, he did. I couldn't get rid of him, and we've been travelling ever since. I tried to get him interested in the female ducks at the Kiwi house, because I couldn't very well take him home with me to England, but he was having none of it, so we left. As far as I know, it isn't against the law to adopt a wild duck. Whether it's against the law for a wild duck to adopt me is another matter.'

Tommy Lee weighed this. 'So, it was okay to try to offload your duck at the Kiwi house, but not okay for them to try to keep it once you'd offloaded it?'

This was a very good point, I felt, but I had an answer for it. I explained that, had Chris been willing to stay, nothing would have given me greater pleasure – with the possible exception of a night of unbridled passion with Halle Berry – but when I realized that Chris wanted to come with me, I had no choice but to take him back again. In other words, the feelings of the duck were paramount. Tommy Lee exhaled slowly. He looked heavenwards and began to examine his ceiling fan. The young rookie hopped from foot to foot and raised his hand eagerly, like schoolboys do when they know the answer.

'Not now, Karl,' snapped Tommy Lee impatiently. 'Can't you see I'm interviewing a criminal here?'

'Excuse me?' I queried, somewhat indignantly.

'A saspict thin,' the officer corrected.

'But sir, it's revelant,' insisted the rookie.

'Or even *relevant*,' I corrected, with a smirk.

Tommy gave me a stare that was meant to sting. 'Go on, Karl,' he sighed.

'I hiv two Jipanese fillers ahtside,' said Karl, mangling my native tongue to the very edge of incomprehensible. 'They say thit they kin prove Mr Eve is innocint.'

'And how, pray, kin they do thit?' asked Tommy Lee.

Karl ushered the two small, fat gentlemen into the room. They bowed. Then the smaller, fatter one spoke.

'Excuse intelluption, but we were at the Kiwi house jus' now, when this man arrested for stearing duck, but I can prove, he no stear duck. It his duck!'

'How kin you possibly know thit?' asked Tommy Lee.

The gentleman produced his pocket digital camera.

'This picture of man with duck in Taupo, by rake. Very funny picture! This another picture of man with duck in ray-by. This one, Waitonga Caves. His duck reary mad with him that day. Very funny picture! It forrow him everywhere; or over New Zearand!'

'The chip at the Kiwi house has rang too,' said Karl, 'and he's changed his mind. He rickons the duck is squawking the place down and going ibsolutely mintal. It's disrupting all the ither birds. Looks like this chip is tilling the truth, ifter all, sir.'

Tommy Lee looked sorely disappointed by this news. This must have been the biggest crime Otorohanga had seen for twenty years, and all of a sudden, his big arrest was melting away like snow on a warm spring day. He massaged his craggy, lined brow and waved a dismissive hand that I took to mean 'bugger off before I go over your motor home and find a bald tyre'. I didn't need telling twice. As I was leaving, he mumbled something to Karl about running me back down to the Kiwi house to pick up my duck and van. At least, that's what I hoped he'd said.

The chap at the Kiwi house looked sheepish, but fell short of an actual apology. He produced Chris from a small holding cage, which they must have used occasionally for troublesome, unruly, antisocial or drunken wildfowl, and upon recognizing me, he went

193

ballistic with excitement. I must admit, it was all rather touching. The chap handed my duck over – I didn't have to sign for it or anything – and we shook hands. Not me and Chris; me and the chap, I mean. I sympathized with his predicament. He was only looking after the welfare of his birds after all, and it's not every day a visitor arrives at a place brim-full of birds with his own personal duck. It's bound to cause confusion. We even had a little laugh about the whole thing in the car park, and Chris joined in, which made us laugh even more. It was just like that part at the end of *Black Beauty* when they're all laughing in the kitchen and the horse's head appears over one of those split farmhouse doors and neighs its approval. *Flipper* was the same at the end, if you recall – heart-warming, if a tad sickly, with everyone sharing a joke, but obviously not at the kitchen door, because Flipper would have dehydrated and died.

Or am I thinking of Skippy?

Ten minutes later, we were well on the way to Te Awamutu, which is just a pleasant, sleepy little town, but it was somewhere I really wanted to see, for sentimental reasons.

Do you remember, at the start of this surreal adventure, I had been troubled by peculiar dreams and insomnia? Well, since I arrived in New Zealand, the dreams had stopped, and I was sleeping like a baby – and by that I don't mean waking up every hour screaming for a feed. If you will recall, at one stage I had a song called, 'I Hope I Never Have to See You Again' constantly playing inside my head like a tape loop. Well, it was written by a band called *Split Enz* that I had followed from the age of sixteen. *Split Enz* was a seventies ex-art college outfit whose members used to dress up like crazed nightmarish marionettes and dance around dysrhythmically on stage, often at odds with the tempo of their music, which takes some doing. Their output was quirky and strange – a little like Lennon and McCartney would have sounded, had they been on some form of hallucinogenic drug. What am I saying? *The Beatles* were *always* on some hallucinogenic drug, come to think about it. This was different though. *Split Enz* often

194

employed quite grand instrumental themes, married with small-town colonial angst, black comedy, music-hall slapstick, rock and roll, thirties-style crooner ballads and even spoon playing. It shouldn't have worked, but it did, and it fascinated me. It was like nothing I'd ever seen or heard before. One typical ballad was called 'Charley', and the gist of it was that two friends and love rivals had had some kind of showdown, culminating in a huge row. The singer takes on the role of one of these rivals, and the morning after their spat is asking the other fellow, Charley, to wake up, draw the blinds, forgive and forget and make a pot of tea, but Charley appears to have shuffled off his mortal coil, and is lying on the settee looking deathly white and still. His rival serenades him, imploring him to open his eyes again, but desperation creeps into his voice as it dawns on him that poor Charley is no more. Every time I listened to their first album, 'Mental Notes', with its echoey, haunting, empty-old-church-hall-with-the-parquet-floor piano sound, I saw in my mind's eye, images of small-town New Zealand or Australia in the fifties. This was very interesting, as the band's founder, Tim Finn, and his younger brother Neil, who eventually went on to form the hugely successful *Crowded House*, came from such a place; Te Awamutu, in fact, the quiet unassuming little town that I was just driving into. I know I'm a bit of a softy, but I swear the hairs on my neck stood on end as I parked the Endeavour next to the lovely white wooden framed church, and saw the sign, 'Welcome to Te Awamutu'. Both Tim and Neil have mentioned the town in their songs, so it seemed very special to me. Tim's 'Haul Away' confirms that he was born in Te Awamutu, 25th June 1952, and the very first song on Neil's inaugural *Crowded House* album also mentions their birthplace with obvious fondness. All along, this holiday had felt more like some form of pilgrimage, and now I had finally reached the holiest place.

I let Chris out for a quick leak on the grass in front of the church, and stowed him away with a bit of bread to keep him quiet. I really did need to research what ducks ate at some stage, as

I feared his current diet was even worse than my son's, back at home.

Almost next to the church was an accountancy firm, and joy of joys, it was Finn and Co., which was founded by the brothers' father, Richard, who now, I was told, resided in an Auckland nursing home. Opposite was the information centre, so I hopped across the road and was delighted to see Finn Brothers posters in the window. There were also Finn Brothers commemorative postage stamps and a map showing all the Finn-related sights in town. I was in my element! The lady behind the counter confided that she never much cared for Tim's music. She thought it weird and added that his hair was also peculiar. They were lovely boys though, she admitted, but somewhat bizarre looking in their early days, and in truth she preferred Jim Reeves. I purchased everything I could get, and set off in search of holy sites. I knew it was deeply sad, but I really didn't care. I found the electrical store where Neil used to work at weekends, and discovered that he often played piano in the street right outside to lure the punters in. I walked up the hill to Te Awamutu Junior School and imagined the two of them playing on the swings and slides in the innocent fifties and sixties. I crossed the road and walked a further few hundred yards until I found their family home, now a rest home, and it struck me, rather poignantly, that old Richard and his recently departed wife, Mary, could feasibly have been residents in a home that was once their own. I then traipsed back to the library, and discovered to my delight that almost half of the building had been transformed into a Finn Brothers museum, and I have to say that it was wonderful. There were old black and white home movies of the boys playing cricket in the garden, or dressing up in silly outfits to amuse the grown-ups (so that's where they got it from!). There were original stage clothes, hand-written lyric sheets and their old, bizarre and arty music videos. I was in heaven, twelve thousand miles from home, but I had no one to share it with, and completely out of the blue, an overwhelming feeling of home-sickness engulfed me, the like of which I had never felt before. All of a sudden, I wanted to hug my children,

196

cuddle my dog and kiss my parents. I even had benign feelings for Katie, my ex-wife.

I sought solace in a small café, purchased a tea and a cheese and ham toastie, and pored over my newly-acquired *Split Enz* memorabilia, just like I used to do when I was sixteen. It even dawned on me what their name meant, finally, after twenty years of following their progress and buying most of their albums. I had noticed all over the country that words ending in 'ds', such as friends, ends, bends, mends and so on, were spelt with an 'nz', to signify New Zealand. *Split Enz* surely referred to the north and south islands. *Split NZ*, in other words. Sometimes, I can be very slow on the uptake. This line of thought made me think of other bands' names, and how they acquired them. My local rock heroes, *Led Zeppelin*, for instance, took their name from a comment that Keith Moon made after appearing at a London club. 'How did you go down?' asked a musician friend. 'Like a lead zeppelin!' he answered. The spelling of 'lead' was changed so that it would always be pronounced correctly, and not like the 'lead' in lead guitarist.

I'm told that Frank Zappa's band were originally called the 'Motherf***ers', but strangely, not many clubs would offer them gigs, so old Frank, realizing that necessity (i.e. the need to eat) is the mother of invention, changed the name to *The Mothers of Invention* – devilishly clever, in my humble opinion.

10cc, the most innocuous of names, was actually very rude. The band read somewhere that the average amount of semen a male ejaculated was 9ccs, so they wanted to go one better. (*The Lovin' Spoonful* used exactly the same inspiration years before.) This set me thinking about what I'd call my band, if I had one – other than in my dreams. If there were four of us, we could be called 'The Four Kinnells', and pretend we were all brothers like *The Osmonds*. If my band was based in nearby Walsall, we could call ourselves 'The Walsall Pact', which is reasonably witty I suppose, but if it was a punk outfit, I'd probably call it 'The Twats' or maybe 'The One-Eyed Trouser Snakes', just to annoy *Daily Mail* readers.

My waitress returned to top up my tea, and spotted my assortment of *Split Enz* leaflets.

'Of course,' she confided, 'Neil used to wait on tables here when he was fifteen, just to earn a few dollars, and my mother went out with his cousin for a bit.'

I was, of course, impressed. I thanked her for the information, swallowed my fifth cup of tea and left. I then spent a lovely, lazy afternoon mooching around the shops, and when the various proprietors or shop assistants realized that I was interested they all chipped in with their own personal Finn story. If they were to be believed, Neil and Tim must have had so many part-time jobs they could barely have spent more than fifteen minutes asleep in ten years. They must have dated every woman within a six-mile radius, played in every bar and attended all seven local schools simultaneously. We have a similar scenario back in Stourbridge where everyone over the age of twenty-seven is a close personal friend of *Led Zeppelin*'s Robert Plant – whatever a close personal friend is. I've yet to meet a distant impersonal one. Maybe the word 'personal' is only applied to those we are desperate to know or in other words, the rich and the famous. I've never heard anyone bother to use the expression to describe their refuse collector or car mechanic mates, that's for sure. Robert's friends tell me what a 'super guy' he is, and how they've got lots of time for him (like their time is worth anything). Amazing how quickly they've assessed his character really, considering they only ever bumped into him once in Kinver's pet shop, and asked for his autograph. Those of his inner circle, however, the ones who have bumped into him twice in the bakery, often refer to him in conversation as 'Bob'. I, for your information, as one who has accidentally bumped into him at least four times, am now entitled to call him 'B', and regard these people as jerks.

I headed back to the white wooden church where I'd left the Endeavour, with a bag of bird food that the Te Awamutu pet shop man had prepared for me, promising that it contained all the essential nutrients, vitamins and minerals that a duck required to not only survive, but thrive. I climbed aboard to a backdrop of grateful quacking – or it may have been nagging; it's difficult to tell – and emptied a sample of this wonder food into a soup bowl for Chris to get his beak into. I have to report that he seemed markedly underwhelmed. He sniffed around for a bit and then ignored it completely, before white-striping the welcome mat in protest. Some ducks are never satisfied. You slave over a hot oven for hours… I ended up chucking him a bit of bread and he wolfed it down, and isn't that typical of the youth of today? Brought up on junk food, and wouldn't know a nutritious meal if it jumped up and bit them.

I had an hour to kill before dinner, so I unwrapped Mr Maori, just to make sure he was still in one piece, and yes, he was, and even uglier than I remembered him. I was very close to Rotorua, and planned to arrive there the following lunchtime, unless of course something unspeakable happened to me, such as being sucked into a black hole whilst travelling along the back road to Putaruru. I intended to check out Rotorua and its famous sulphur pools in the day, before treating myself to a Maori cultural evening with traditional food and entertainment. The following day, I would seek out the Maori Museum and get down to business. Then, once the ugly little wooden bastard-cum-meal ticket had been delivered, and duly photographed with me and the Curator, I was planning to head off to a very special place called Kare Kare, which *Crowded House* fans would have heard of. It is a wild and beautiful place that feels as if it were at the very end of the earth; the sort of place that cartographers used to label with the warning, 'Here be Dragons'. It boasts tropical rainforests, waterfalls, a handful of wonderful houses scattered around the valley, and nothing beyond it but thousands of miles of mighty, roaring ocean. The 'Together Alone' album was recorded there, in a private house high above the beach, and I already knew exactly

199

what the place looked like, because the band made a video of how
the album was conceived. They even hired a full Maori choir and
drummers to give the music a spiritual sound, and I really wanted
to see it in the flesh; to walk that beach, and run down that forest
path and sit at the foot of the waterfall as they had done in their
video diary. After that, I was going to drive to Ninety Mile Beach,
and then over to the Bay of Islands, before finally heading for
Auckland and then home. All very adventurous for someone who
had baulked at the idea of stepping onto the plane in the first
place.

That evening, I finally got round to doing what I had planned to
do on numerous occasions. After the obligatory Blue Cod supper,
I settled into the umpteenth Top Tin site of my stay, cracked open
a bottle of red and set about reading Uncle Ken's bundle of letters,
with my faithful duck by my side.

What I found surprised me a little, but touched me a lot.
Virtually every letter was from a Maori lady named Aroha, and it
was fairly obvious to the meanest intelligence – and by that I refer
to myself – that this woman was the love of his life, and vice
versa. The letters were in chronological order, and read like
Shakespeare's *Romeo and Juliet*. Unfortunately, this included the
tragic part. Old Aroha's folks were less than thrilled at the
prospect of their precious daughter marrying the likes of Ken, and
the reasons they stated required several sheets of foolscap. Chief
among these was the fact that he was white and English.
Secondary ones included him being in the Merchant Navy, and as
such, they feared he would have an Aroha (which means 'love') in
every port. Oh yes, and there were two other things they
disapproved of, namely, everything he said, and everything he did.
The strange thing was, on the evidence of these letters, Uncle Ken
seemed to be the very model of propriety and sobriety in those
days, unlike the later incarnation that I knew. Admittedly, it was
difficult to get the whole picture just by reading the woman's
correspondence and without having access to Ken's replies, but
there was something about the tone of these poignant letters that

200

told me she was writing to a good-natured, sincere, even-tempered – abstemious even – and totally besotted man. Here was a union made in heaven, but frowned upon down here on earth. All of a sudden, I was beginning to realize that my uncle made the regrettable transformation from saint to sinner only when his world was turned upside down for him, courtesy of his lover's parents. Not once did the letters hint of her parents' displeasure with the many hedonistic traits with which I associated him. I searched for juicy little snippets such as, 'Ma says, if you ever vomit in her cooking pot again after a night on the rum, she will castrate you!' But alas, none were found. It seemed that poor Ken had bent over backwards to fit in, but had been met with a brick wall. There was no way on earth they would ever allow their daughter to marry anyone but a 'dyed in the wool' Maori lad, and that was that. As the letters progressed, it became obvious that their liaisons, once so public, had now become clandestine affairs. Aroha had resorted to subterfuge in order to stay with her man, and had hinted darkly that, should she ever be found out, all hell would break loose.

I devoured every letter that evening, eager and impatient for the next instalment. Earlier, I had compared them to *Romeo and Juliet*, but they also read like a Jane Austen novel, such were their brooding intensity and the frustration of the two central characters. I could sense that something truly awful was about to happen, as their relationship became more and more doomed. Here was a love affair that was the equal of Anne and Captain Wentworth's, Cathy and Heathcliffe's, or even David and Victoria's. I was becoming totally hooked, as my pile of unread letters was becoming ever thinner. After several more heart-wrenching outpourings of emotion from an increasingly dispirited-sounding young girl, I was finally down to my last letter. It was then that everything became clear, and I fully realized what I was doing in New Zealand.

My Uncle Ken had had his young heart broken, thanks to Aroha's parents' refusal to accept him, and any slim chance he had of winning their acceptance had been blown out of the water, thanks to ten awful minutes in Rotorua, way back in 1973. Things, it seemed, had come to a head, and the besotted young Aroha had been caught canoodling with Ken on the lake. Even canoeing would have been bad enough for a harsh disciplinarian such as Aroha's father, but the sight of his daughter kissing the man in the white uniform after he had expressly forbidden it, was too much. He had, from what I could glean, waded in and forcefully separated them, giving Ken a punch on the jaw for good measure. Ken, who I know used to box for the navy, responded by instinctively flattening Aroha's father, before he had even ascertained the identity of his assailant. Punching someone's lights out is seldom the best way to endear oneself to that person, and so it proved with these two. What had previously been a frosty relationship now became positively arctic, and Ken was warned that, if he ever set foot in the town again, he would be clubbed, cooked and eaten, even though the Maoris had officially denounced that kind of behaviour many years previously. Aroha was told in no uncertain terms that if she saw him again she would be ex-communicated, or whatever the equivalent was for Maoris – clubbed, cooked and eaten probably. She obviously did her fair share of sobbing, weighed her man against her family, friends and traditions, and hollowly agreed to toe the party line, broken-hearted as she undoubtedly was. Incensed by this rejection, Ken must have flipped his lid and begun his descent into Oliver Reed-style behaviour. He got himself roaring drunk, smashed his way into the Maori Museum – which his sweetheart's parents owned and ran – and after a bit of heart-felt graffiti work and some wanton vandalism, absconded with the most treasured artefact he could find, as a memento of his tortured and ill-fated romance. This final letter, no doubt written through a veil of tears, was Aroha's goodbye.

I dropped it onto the table and sighed a heavy sigh. I was the one that Ken had chosen to tie up the loose ends – to make amends posthumously for what he'd done. Now, all sorts of strange thoughts were jockeying for pole position in my head. Would anyone mentioned in the letters still be at the museum? Would Aroha's dad be waiting for me with a studded club, eager to snuff out the life of anyone remotely related to his old nemesis? It was all very well for Mr Chance the solicitor to say they'd welcome me like a long-lost brother, but he didn't know about the contents of the letters did he? This wasn't just the return of a valuable artefact we were talking about here. I was the nephew of a man who had probably busted the museum Curator's nose. I couldn't see that endearing him to me, if he was still alive and kicking. All of a sudden, I could understand why this jaunt was worth a quarter of a million quid. It was danger money!

That night I tossed and turned in bed, worried sick about coming face to face with this man. I drew some comfort from the fact that he would now be quite old, which meant I could probably outrun him, if push came to shove. Depressingly, the old insomnia had returned to haunt me, after nearly three stress-free weeks, and it must have been at least five o'clock before I dropped off properly. It didn't help matters having a pet duck that always seemed to want a shit at three-thirty a.m. On the plus side, he did seem to be getting the hang of asking to be let out, rather than striping the settee, the way he used to.

Just as I'd managed to drop off, something dropped onto my face as I lay in bed, followed by a very sharp stabbing pain under my eye. I reached up and turned on the dismal twenty watt reading light, just in time to see something small and brown scurry off under the duvet. I lifted it up in horror, and suddenly they swarmed all over me, hundreds of them, stabbing me with their little spears. There must have been two hundred little Maori warriors, just like the one I'd bought from the gift shop, and they were jabbing me all over my body, like crazed little acupuncturists. I tried whacking them onto the floor with the backs of my hands, but for every one I flicked off, twenty more appeared from nowhere, chanting and spitting out that horrible, frightening Haka war dance that they do – a bit like the warriors do in *Zulu* before they storm the fort. I tried to get out of bed, but a gang of them were tying me down with ropes, like I was Gulliver. Then, heading across the breakfast table in massive battalions, like something I'd seen in films about the Roman Empire, were hundreds of tiny Kiwis, their long, sharp beaks glinting like steel blades in the gloom. They were leaping from the table like lemmings, landing on my face and chest, and lacerating me with their built-in swords. I screamed with pain as one of them pierced my eye, and woke up sweating and hyperventilating, observed by a concerned-looking Mallard.

Aren't dreams so bloody annoying? Had I been awake, I would obviously have known that plagues of three-inch tall Maoris simply didn't infest duvets, and regiments of Kiwis didn't march across breakfast tables. In a dream, however, you take it all in, hook, line and sinker, don't you? It all seems so plausible. I glanced across to the table and spotted the little plastic and possum fur bastards that had sparked off this latest nightmare, looking all innocent and nonchalant, propped up behind the Shiraz bottle. The Kiwi seemed to be perusing my deck of cards with interest, as if to say, 'Nothing to do with me, mate!'

Yeah! Pull the other one. They were both going in the nearest skip when I rolled into Rotorua.

It was fair to say that I'd mellowed by the time I got there, and I had graciously granted the pair of them a stay of execution, figuring that it was my overly fertile imagination, rather than their direct involvement, that had resulted in my latest night-time trauma. Besides, they would make two decent small presents for the kids when I got home, and I wasn't made of money. Well, not yet anyway.

I located the Top Tin – I'm such a creature of habit – and made my way to town to find the local information centre. A short time later, I emerged with a ticket for that evening's Maori Experience – a show plus traditional dinner – which was a short coach ride away. Conveniently, my camp site was one of the three allocated pick-up points, which meant I could leave the van hooked up for

204

the evening and have a few drinks at the event. I also remembered to pick up a map – to show me where the various hot springs and geyser sites were situated – and a leaflet about the Maori Museum.

That afternoon, after I'd ensured Chris was fed, exercised and watered, I caught the bus in search of thermal activity. Rather worryingly, the entire area was riddled with such places, like a huge, unpredictable cauldron waiting to erupt. There were even little bubbling pools of yellow, sulphur-coloured water by the side of the road, belching out steam, and the smell was just awful, like everyone within five square miles had decided to eat rotten eggs and fart at the same time. I suppose the locals just got used to it, but at first it was so pungent it made me want to retch. The site for which I'd purchased a ticket was, in spite of its appalling smell, quite incredible. The whole area reminded me of those bleak, doomsday films that portray a country after a nuclear war. There was a succession of barren landscapes with fossilized trees, and huge, bubbling hot pools in completely unnatural colours that would have names such as Sulphur Yellow, Acid Green or Phosphorescent Pink, if they were a B&Q paint range. Sometimes, the steam coming from these hellish lakes was so dense that fellow visitors would appear like hooded ghouls from them without warning and scare the living daylights out of me. There were huge holes in the ground, with names such as The Devil's Cooking Pot, which spat and hissed their threats to passers-by. I wondered if there was one in the vicinity called The Devil's Arsehole. Judging by the smell, it was obviously nearby, and it seemed that Old Lucifer had a penchant for ten-thousand egg omelettes. It did occur to me that I had flown twelve thousand miles to see some of the most wonderful views in the world, and here I was spending the afternoon in surely the most inhospitable place I've ever been to, and definitely the smelliest. I have to admit that I did find it fascinating, but, call me old-fashioned, I like leaves on trees, birdsong and clear blue water with fish in it. This was a tad too similar to Hiroshima for my taste, and I was longing to get back to the pleasant stuff.

I flagged down my bus and headed back to the site. I needed to shave, iron a shirt and dry my best trousers at the launderette ready for my Big Night Out. Three weeks living in a motor home – one of which was spent co-habiting with an incontinent duck – had changed my appearance from suave Nicholas Cage look-alike to Trafalgar Square Big Issue salesman, and I needed to smarten up. You never know who you might meet at these events, after all.

CHIPTAH 16

In which I have a life-changing Maori experience.

The coach dropped us off in a large tarmaced clearing within a dense area of rainforest, and drove off again. We were met by a young Maori man with a huge, toothy grin that resembled Richard Pryor. Obviously, it was the man that resembled Richard Pryor, not just his grin, though the grin did resemble Richard's grin as well, if you see what I mean. He shepherded us into reception, gave us all badges and asked us to follow him down a winding, illuminated path into the woods. He marched off in front with his torch, all the time firing his well-rehearsed jokes at us to make us feel at ease. I did think though that the gag about Maoris having finally voted the previous week, to officially denounce their old, cannibalistic ways, was ill-chosen – delivered, as it was, in pitch darkness, halfway down a secluded forest path. The American lady next to me seemed to become a little faint at this point, and I had to explain to her the concept of jokes. I suppose she was worried because she would have provided food for a whole tribe for months, if things turned nasty. Had I been Hannibal Lecter, I'd have been on the mobile, asking Curry's if they stocked industrial-sized freezers.

The path eventually led to a small river, which was magically lit by rows of flaming bulrushes. Richard Pryor stopped at this point to address the crowd, the contents of three coaches in all, which probably numbered at least one hundred and fifty people. He explained that the Maori warriors travelled around the various islands that made up New Zealand in long, narrow, hand-carved canoes, chanting their war cries as they rowed. Then he asked us to be silent, and we stood there, shivering in the darkness, waiting for something to happen.

For a minute or two nothing did, and then, faraway in the distance, we heard them coming, and I have to say that it made the hairs on my neck stand up. Then, gradually, the haunting sound got nearer and we could see them. I turned on the camcorder and filmed them arriving in their boat, heavily tattooed, wild, scary eyes darting wildly this way and that, and huge tongues leering out of their grotesque mouths. God, it was impressive! They raised their oars in unison and chanted something fairly intimidating at us all. For all I know it was probably just, 'Lovely to see you folks, how are you?' but it made the huge American lady blanch beneath her tan, and she had to clutch onto a tree for support.

Luckily for her, the warriors slipped back onto their boat after that and paddled on into the dark again, giving us a wonderful view of their naked backsides as they did so. This, I'm pleased to report, seemed to bring some of the colour back to her cheeks.

Back at the ranch, we were shown the Hāngi, which was the conventional way the Maori cooked food for the tribe. Everything was wrapped in traditional silver kitchen-foil, and dropped into a shallow hole in the ground on top of white-hot coals. Old Richard joked that we would later have to run barefoot across this area, and once more Miss Fat America drained of colour. Do these Americans actually believe every single thing they are told? Their naïveté is almost childlike.

While dinner was being prepared, we were herded into an auditorium for the show, and I bagged myself a front seat. The stage was a recreation of a traditional old Maori village, with mud huts, palm trees and a sandy floor, and once we had all settled, Richard stepped on stage to formally introduce himself. He wise-cracked for five minutes or so, and then asked for a volunteer from the audience to come up on stage, so that the cast could enact the

210

'stranger in the village' scene. This is the one where someone enters the Maori village and is challenged by the warriors – think Captain Cook here, if it helps. They go into their ritual of sizing up the newcomer – dancing around him a bit to cure his constipation – and then offer him a token of their friendship. He must accept it in the correct way (which begs the question, how on earth does he know what that *is* if he's never set foot on the island before?), and according to his response, they either spear him to death and turn him into a human kebab, or embrace him like a long-lost relative. All good old corny tourist fare of course, but impressive nevertheless. The poor Dutch lad they chose looked terrified, and who could blame him? The Maori warriors have this disconcerting knack of madly rolling their eyes, bobbing their fifteen-inch tongues out and hissing like serpents, a few inches away from your face. Call me old-fashioned, but there's no need for it. Surely, they could just offer the stranger their business card and shake hands like we do. One tattooed bloke kept prancing around with a sharp spear, jabbing away in the poor chap's direction as if about to strike. If this was a welcome, I'd hate to see a disagreement. Then, after five minutes of this intimidating behaviour, he lays something at the feet of the stranger, or Dutchman in this case, and waits for a reaction. I couldn't quite make out what he was offering, but it looked as if it were crafted from possum fur. The Dutchman duly picked it up, as instructed by Richard Pryor, and launched into his hastily-learnt speech, which was basically, 'We come in peace, old chap. When can we all have our dinner?'

This seemed to pacify the spear chucker, who retreated into the chorus, and began singing a lovely South Sea Islands-type tune, while hanging garlands of flowers around the Dutchman's neck. They were accompanied by a chap playing a traditional Yamaha twelve string acoustic, another bloke on the bongos and three women blowing on giant conch shells.

Then I saw her.

A beautiful, dark-skinned maiden of around thirty-five summers stepped forward from the choir and began to sing. She looked very much like Halle Berry with shoulder-length black curly hair, and she was wearing no more than a swim suit affair made out of dried grass. Her arms waved around in that enchanting way that Hawaiians favour for accompanying their singing, and her voice was every bit as beautiful as her face.

I sat there mesmerized. I literally couldn't take my eyes off her for a second, and I know it's silly to say that this was love at first sight, but, from my point of view, it was. Once she'd finished her solo, she slipped back into the throng again, but by that time, I had eyes for no one else. Even when the men performed a stirring Haka, all I could think about was drinking her in. My eyes must have been burning a hole in her gorgeous, naked flesh, because she suddenly became aware of me, sat there in the front row, drooling, and smiled. Well, this just about did for me, I can tell you. I felt my spine dissolve and I slumped into the chair, reddening at the cheeks like a coy ten-tear-old. This seemed to delight the girl, and she had to smother a grin and concentrate on a rather complex dance routine, which involved a lot of wild eye-rolling and tongue-bobbing. For some reason, this made me fancy her even more. What I had previously thought of as menacing and sinister, suddenly I now found deeply erotic. Fully aware at this point that I was glued to her every move, she deliberately began to aim her tongue waggling at me, firing up her wild eyes as she did so. It was as if she were performing an ancient courtship ritual just for me, and I could feel my mini pocket-boomerang responding in no uncertain terms, if you will excuse the completely incorrect cultural reference. Call me ignorant, but I really have no idea whatsoever what Maori warriors carry in their trousers, and nor do I wish to find out, thank you very much.

A few more tribal dances, a choreographed but extremely violent fight routine with large sticks, followed by a nice sing-song, and it was all over, and I for one was charmed off my feet. All of a sudden, I loved the Maori culture, the way of life, the singing, everything. Even the tattoos. I was besotted. The cast exited stage left, followed shortly afterwards by the starving crowd, and I was left bereft and crestfallen. She had been snatched from me in the cruellest way, and I would probably never see her again. I just sat there stunned and bewildered, in a world of my own, and then a voice said, 'Aren't you hungry?'

I looked up, and she was sitting on the edge of the stage.

'Oh, yes, er, yes, yes. Yes I am,' I gibbered.

'Yis, yis, yis, yis you are?' she mocked.

'I love the way you say yis,' I drooled.

'Yis?' she asked.

'Yis,' I confirmed. 'Can I, erm, buy you a, you know, drink in the restaurant, or do you have to, sort of, get dressed or whatever?'

'I hiv to git drissed,' she smiled.

'Oh, I'm sorry to erm …'

'But I'll be in there in five minutes, if thit's okay.'

I told her that it was more than okay. I dragged myself from the chair and staggered next door into the dining area. I had an allocated place on a table full of Germans, so I hung around by the bar instead. It was an easy choice. Exactly five minutes later – and believe me, I was counting the seconds – she walked in, and I couldn't have been more excited without penile incontinence. She was wearing a skimpy white top that made her skin look even darker, and a pair of figure-hugging cut-off jeans. There were four inches of flat, brown stomach just above them, and it was all I could do to stop myself from dashing over and licking it.

'Hi,' she smiled. 'God, you must think I'm so forward, you know, just …'

213

'That's exactly what I was about to say,' I laughed. 'Only, I'm a bit worried about even saying hello to you, after this thing I've been reading.'

'Thing?'

'Well, correspondence really. You don't have a big burly chap lurking around the corner who'd disembowel me just for talking to you, do you?'

'What are you on about? Hiv you been on the booze before you've eaten dinner? Thit's fatal!'

'No, no,' I insisted. 'I thought nice Maori girls weren't permitted to, you know, mix with whites, kind of thing.'

'What?' she laughed, incredulously. 'Where did you read thit? Was this a Victorian book?'

'No. More like the 1970s really. It's just that this Maori girl in the story ... Well, never mind. So your folks are relaxed about that kind of thing?'

She looked at me as if I were a cute but thick three-year-old.

'Will, I only hiv my mother, but she's so laid back about *thit kind of thing* it's untrue. Actually, she's usually here singing with me, but she's gone to Kare Kare to buy an antique jewellery box or something, so you're quite safe, and she stopped carrying a spear, well, weeks ago.'

My ears pricked up. 'Kare Kare you say? I was going there next. I'm touring around your beautiful country in a Kore-Take motor home, you see. I wanted to go there because *Crowded House* ...'

'Recorded 'Together Alone' there. I know. I was there.'

'You were there?'

'Yis. You know they used a Maori choir on the album? Guess who was one of the singers!'

214

Well, I was in love anyway, but that snippet of information sealed it. I even had the video at home, so she would have been on it. I gawped at her with eyes like saucers. 'That's my favourite track on my favourite album! And that was *you*?'

'Yis!'

'So you actually know Neil Finn then?'

'Yis!'

'I do really love when you say 'yis'. Can I see you tomorrow for lunch or something?'

'Yis!'

'Do you really know Neil Finn? Everyone in New Zealand claims to know him.'

'It's a small place, and musicians seem to know other musicians I suppose. It's not like in England, where Rock Gods like Lid Zipellin are inaccessible and live in huge estates with electronic gates, you know.'

I ordered two drinks and we sat down on a couple of spare seats. I had a bit of information to impart about my close friend Bob, and I wanted it to impress her.

For the rest of the evening, we talked, laughed, exchanged *Split Enz* and *Crowded House* stories, ate food that had been cooked in a hole in the ground (and I don't mean Slough), gazed into each other's eyes, and by half-eleven, we were holding hands. I felt as if I'd died and gone to Maori heaven. The strange thing was, she seemed equally besotted with me, and call me self-effacing if you will, but previously I couldn't really imagine that ever happening. How could I expect anyone else to like me if I didn't even like myself? I tended to skip past the mirror in my house because I wasn't too fond of the chap looking back at me. He looked far too much like my dad, and always appeared to be at least ten years

215

older than I knew I was. You get what you pay for with these cheap Ikea mirrors I suppose. Even in the early days of my courtship and eventual marriage, it was never like this. I remember kissing Katie, but for some reason I can't recall her ever kissing *me*, if you know what I mean. She just held her lips still and let me move mine about instead. No passion about sums it up. I tried to recall the times she'd spontaneously flung an arm around me in bed. It was easy. She never had.

Then, without warning, it was suddenly time to go home on the coach, and people began to shuffle out. I felt like Prince Charming must have felt when he had to part company with Cinderella, but in reverse. It was I who was about to jump on the coach and disappear, not my new friend. I toyed with the idea of dropping one of my Adidas trainers as I left, in the hope that she would retrieve it and start asking around the Top Tin sites after me, but things have moved on a lot since the eighteenth century, so I asked for her mobile number instead. She walked outside to the car park with me and we stood spellbound under a giant canopy of stars. I swear the night sky is ten times clearer than in England, and it boasts ten million or more extra stars too. It had got very chilly and she wasn't wearing too much, so I gallantly cuddled her to stop her shivering. Jeez, it was heaven. She suddenly seemed so small and vulnerable, and you'll never believe what happened next. A shooting star whizzed across the firmament, like some kind of sign that this liaison was intended to be. I kissed her warm, full lips and she kissed mine back, only more so, to the power of ten, with knobs on. Here I was, twelve thousand miles from home, under the stars with a beautiful woman, kissing. Then the coach driver honked his horn by way of reminding me that he had a coach full of Germans, Dutch, Americans and Australians, but no Englishman. I promised to phone the following morning and she promised to take me sightseeing, and then show me where the museum was. She escorted me to the coach steps and I quickly kissed her one last time. It suddenly dawned on me that we had been talking non-stop for over an hour, but I still didn't know her name or what she did for a living, and vice versa.

216

'It's Kura,' she smiled, 'and I'm a journalist on the local Rotorua paper.'

'I'm Adam,' I replied, 'and I'm a writer too! We have so much in common, we're like twins.'

'I hope not,' she laughed. 'Twins can't be lovers.'

I climbed the steps and sheepishly strode down to the back of the coach, past sniggering passengers. I sat down and quickly wiped away the condensation on the window, so I could see her one last time before the morning. I don't think I have ever felt such overwhelming happiness. It was as if all my senses were heightened. I waved, she blew a kiss, and we were gone into the night.

CHIPTAH 17

In which Chris chats up a bird.

I got back to the Endeavour at a quarter to twelve, elated but also fretful. I let Chris out for his constitutional waddle around, taking great care not to fall over any picnic benches or set off any high-pressure hoses whilst doing so. At around midnight, I was just getting undressed for bed when the mobile rang. It was either feast or famine with my phone: nothing for ages and then a flood of calls all at once. The 58 bus from Dudley to Wolverhampton was prone to behave in similar fashion, if I remember rightly; the frequency of it, I mean.

The first call was from my children, asking if I was still alive, and this really put the cat amongst the pigeons, mentally speaking. On the one hand, I had two kids back at home, and on the other, a woman I'd only known for two hours that I adored, conveniently situated as far away from England as it was possible to get without getting closer again. We chatted for ages and I felt my stomach turn over as I wished them goodnight. As I dropped my phone onto the breakfast table with trembling hand, a little sensible voice inside me told me to stop behaving like a lovesick twelve-year-old, grow up, and face my responsibilities. Jack, my young lad, had earnestly explained to me how he had volunteered to walk around the cricket pitch seven times to help a lad that had 'spinal beefeater'. I hadn't an inkling how walking around a pitch seven times could possibly help the poor child, but then again, I still, to this day, can't work out why sending milk bottle tops or old

219

envelopes with the stamps attached help *Blue Peter* to buy stuff for African schools. I was also concerned about this new illness that Jack had invented, which, if anything, sounded even worse than the real thing. To his credit though, he was always volunteering for worthy-sounding fund-raising activities. I remember being horrified when Katie told me that he had put his name down for backpacking in Iceland, because it would somehow benefit a girl in his class who had cancer. I complained to his school in the strongest possible terms that a child of his age wasn't ready for such potentially dangerous expeditions, no matter how worthy the cause, and was greeted by nonplussed indifference. I felt such a fool, once they'd explained to me that no child, as far as they were aware, had ever been injured packing bags in an Iceland store, and then hinted that I was being over-protective. You should have heard what I called Katie that evening when she got home from work. Well, maybe you shouldn't.

Now, after hearing his innocent little voice, I had tears welling up in my eyes and I didn't have a clue what to do. I'd met someone I really liked, but I knew next to nothing about her. For all I knew, she could be married to a psychotic thug. Even worse, she could be a psychotic thug herself, though I very much doubted it. Neither of us was in the first flush of youth either, so she surely must have had a history, if you know what I mean. Then again, so did I, so I couldn't very well judge. And, my timing, as usual, was impeccable. I couldn't have met her on the first day and had four glorious weeks with her. Oh no! I had to fall in love on the last week of my trip instead, knowing full well that within a few days we were destined to part company. I'd seen the expression 'the tyranny of distance' used somewhere, maybe in a poem I'd learnt at school, but all of a sudden I knew exactly what it's author meant by it. I could hardly pop over for long weekends could I? And it was downright arrogant to expect that she should meekly follow me back to the Mother Country for the sake of love.

The phone rang again, and it was mom and dad. Len the psychic dog was quite happy, apart from when mom had to drag him to the

ets for his booster and to be weighed, but the real reason for
inging was that he'd created another one of his scatological
predictions the previous evening, and she wanted to fill me in.
Apparently, his poo resembled a set of rugby posts with a perfect
E' next to them. Well, this was a new one for me. I told her I'd
never seen him do anything remotely similar before, and I'd have
o ponder it a while and get back to her. It wasn't as if there was a
ibrary book on the subject that I could take out and study, after
ll, though I must admit that I did think about writing one.

No sooner than I'd said goodbye, the phone rang yet again, and
his time it was Mr Chance the solicitor asking if I'd been to the
museum yet. I explained that I was intending to go the next
afternoon, after I'd spent the morning with the love of my life. She
knew exactly where the place was and was going to take me there
after a spot of canoeing on the lake. This seemed to satisfy him,
and he hung up, just in time for the phone to ring once more. It
was Kura, and my heart leapt into my mouth. She'd just phoned to
say how much she'd enjoyed her evening and to tell me where her
house was, so that I could pick her up at tin the next day. She lived
n a small, colonial-style bungalow with two acres of land at the
back, near Rainbow Springs, and it sounded idyllic. I blew her a
kiss, told her I couldn't wait, and we said goodnight.

As if I hadn't got enough on my plate, I was very concerned
about Chris. In a way, he was the duck version of Kura, except of
course that he was male and I wasn't in love with him. What I
mean is, I'd foolishly allowed him to get too close to me, and now
he was institutionalized (most people who get close to me end up
institutionalized for some reason). The minutes were ticking away
to when I was going to have to abandon him, and I knew it would
break his heart, and mine. I should never have allowed myself to
become friendly with him. I should have been a rock; an island;
because *a rock feels no pain, and an island never cries*. As Paul
Simon once said. I just knew that I was going to have to hand the
Endeavour back in Auckland with a frightened little Mallard
clinging onto my leg and sobbing, 'Don't leave me!'

The sentimental tears that I had shed for my children had only just dried, and now new ones were welling up once more. I had got myself into all sorts of trouble again. Why couldn't I just walk through life minding my own business?

I crawled into bed and lay there for ages, staring at the ceiling and thinking of Kura. It's strange, don't you think, that we find girlfriend or boyfriend, usually within a five-mile radius of where we live, and after a couple of months of courtship – to use charming old expression – we swear that these people are our soul mates, and the only person in the world for us. If this is true, then it's a hell of a coincidence that they are conveniently situated geographically speaking. I mean, what are the odds of that realistically? It's far more sensible to admit that there are thousands upon thousands of potential soul mates situated in all corners of the world, and all we've done is locate one of the many suitable ones locally. Only with me, I found one so ridiculously far away that it was going to cause nothing but heartache, unless of course she was willing to throw away all she had in New Zealand to come and live with me in Stourbridge. Either that or I had to abandon my kids, parents and dog to start a new life in New Zealand. Well, put simply like that, there wasn't a problem. It all became as clear as day. I'd simply borrow a Smith and Wesson and blow my brains out instead. Why oh why hadn't I met someone from Dudley, or Birmingham, or Wolverhampton, like everyone else did round my way? It would have been far easier. Surely they didn't *all* have bleached, straightened hair and a tattoo of a dolphin in the small of their back. There were probably at least three equally suitable soul mates within a five-mile radius of my flat, if I only knew where to look. Why had it been necessary to travel to the ends of the flipping earth to fall in love?

I resolved to calm down and stop getting ahead of myself. After all, this holiday romance – and that, much as I hated to admit it, was what it was – could fizzle out the following day over an argument about nothing. She could see me in the cold light of day and change her mind. These things happen. Have you ever fancied someone driving the car behind you, in your rear-view mirror? It is a well-known fact that women look sixty-two per cent sexier in rear-view mirrors than in real life. You pull into a motorway services for petrol and they do too, and when you get out you realize that Brigitte Bardot has morphed into a chain-smoking Eastenders-style barmaid grandmother with teeth that would have looked better in a horse. Perhaps Kura wouldn't look quite so hot in the morning.

Or perhaps I was talking a load of shite.

The truth was, I couldn't get her off my mind, and I spent hours tossing and turning – mainly tossing to be honest – until I finally must have dozed off. I always remember my grandmother's remedy for insomnia. Lie on the very edge of the bed, she'd say, and you'll soon drop off. Well, it amused me at the time, but in fairness, I was only a small boy.

I was showered, shaved and breakfasted by half-eight, which was most unusual for me. Since I'd been in New Zealand, I'd been waking up later and later each day as I think I mentioned, so this was an indication of how excited I was. I consulted my expensive map, and set off towards Rainbow Springs. Eventually, after a couple of the now mandatory wrong turns, I fetched up in front of a perfect little whitewashed frame-house with a green corrugated roof and a front porch created from beautiful intricate fretwork, as is traditional. There were tubs of pretty flowers, several wicker baskets full of chopped logs and a dozy cream-coloured Labrador stretched across the doorway that must have weighed sixteen stone. I told Chris to wait in the van for me and I strode down the path with my bunch of flowers – a nice, last minute idea which I hoped would go down big. Negotiating the snoring mound of furry canine fat proved difficult, but eventually I managed to ring the doorbell with my forehead, and a few seconds later, Kura appeared, looking so wonderful I nearly had an accident. Her hair was tied back now, revealing a long, elegant neck just built for kissing, and she was wearing a man's white shirt with rolled-up sleeves, and a pair of faded jeans with a hole in the knee. Her soulful eyes looked completely black, like a songbird's, with no discernable pupils, and her teeth were the purest white. She also had a smile that was considerably bigger than the legal limit, which I deem to be essential in a female. I handed her the flowers and she laughed at me.

'Joe's Garage, the Old Taupo Road!' she said. 'You shouldn't have!'

'Is it that obvious?' I asked, hurt.

'There's a clue in the pink paper they use to wrap around them,' she explained. 'It says, in huge letters, 'Joe's Garage, Old Taupo Road'. It's a repeat pattern, like wallpaper, see!'

I gave her my best ashamed look, hoping she'd feel sorry for me and kiss me with those fulsome lips of hers, and do you know what? She did, and she flung her lovely arms around me too.

'Let's go out the back and I'll show you my new garden,' she smiled. 'It's ripper!'

We walked outside into the beautiful warm sunshine, and were greeted by a ginger cat.

'Oh, I hope you like animals,' said Kura, as the creature entwined itself around her perfectly-formed legs. 'It's like a menagerie out here.'

I stood admiring her garden, which I told her looked very English.

'Oh, thank you!' she replied. 'Praise indeed. I've always wanted to go to England. The gardens look so wonderful, from what I've seen in magazines. I tried to make mine look like an English cottage garden. Look, I even have a duck pond, like you have in your quaint villages.'

There was indeed a duck pond, and it had a duck floating on it which interested me, for personal reasons.

'Ah, thit's Henrietta' she said. 'I'm afraid I only have one duck so far. It's a new pond, and the local ducks haven't discovered it yit, apart from her. She's got a damaged wing, so she can't fly off you see. When she first arrived, she got into a fight with my stupid dog -- the one you nearly fell over just now. He tried to eat her, but I showed him the error of his ways with a swift kick up the arse. Now they've become quite friendly, thank God. Anyway, thit's why I call her Henrietta.'

'What is?' I asked, puzzled.

'Oh, did I miss out the important bit? I'm always doing thit! I'd be a useless comedienne; I forget the punch line. My dog's called Henry. Henry ate her. See?'

The girl was every bit as deranged as I was. This was most encouraging.

'Erm, I have a pet duck too!' I told her. 'His name is Chris Piddock. He's waiting in the van. Can I go and get him?'

Kura gave me the kind of look that a psychiatrist gives a patient who remarks that the Rorschach Ink Blot Test he has been asked to study reminds him of a nun's genitalia. We returned to the front garden and walked up the path to the Endeavour, with Kura flashing me quizzical looks every now and again, like she'd inadvertently got mixed up with a certifiable nutter and was regretting it. I opened the side door and Chris waddled out. Seeing him do so, it dawned on me that I had missed the ideal surname for him. I should have named him Chris Waddle, after the England footballer. I picked him up and introduced him to my new girlfriend. It was important for me that they got on, obviously. Kura stroked him gently, and I could see that Chris approved.

'I won't ask why you're travelling around New Zealand with a Mallard duck,' she said, scratching her head. 'No, wait a minute. I have to. Why are you travelling around New Zealand with a Mallard duck?'

I explained my predicament in great detail, and she stood transfixed, breaking off just occasionally to fall about laughing. She suggested introducing Chris to Henrietta, and I said I'd give it a try, but I didn't hold much hope. I related the unfortunate Kiwi house incident, which again had the woman in near hysterics, but we both agreed that it was worth a go, in the absence of plan B.

I carried Chris over Henry's comatose body – wondering how he'd ever summoned up enough energy to chase a duck in the first place – and through the house into the garden. I placed him on the grass and sat with Kura, drinking tea and holding hands like a pair of teenagers. Henrietta soon waddled over to inspect him, sniffed around a bit and waddled back to her pond. Then, miracle of miracles, Chris waddled over to join her. Kura had built a little island in the middle of her pond, with a small replica of her own wooden house, for Henrietta to sleep in, safe from predators, and it was into this house she now retired.

Chris reached the water's edge, and I swear he glanced back at me, as if unsure what to do next. Then he slid into the pond, paddled over to the island and sheepishly waddled into the wooden house. I was fully expecting all hell to break loose, but all was silent. Could it be that this was love at first sight once more? Had Henrietta broken the bond between man and duck? In a way, I was quite upset by it all, I have to admit, and had I not had a beautiful woman to take my mind off it I daresay I would have been even more upset. All things considered though, I was mightily relieved that nature seemed to have taken its course at last.

I turned my attentions to the lovely Kura, and, biting the bullet, asked her if she was married or dating a fifteen-stone wrestler with psychotic tendencies. She told me that she had been married for a short time to a Maori man who was okay until he moved in with her, and then he got drunk a lot and treated her like dirt. She had tied the knot far too young, and though her wise, tolerant mother knew from the very start that it wasn't a marriage made in heaven, she had kept her council, even though it had hurt to do so. Less than a year later it was all over, and Kura had been single ever since. Occasionally she'd been on dates with local men, but no one had exactly set her alight, until halfway through a song at the previous night's Maori evening, when a loony Englishman began pulling funny faces at her.

Then she asked about my background. I explained my situation, and the fact that I had two young children back at home. I told her that I was approaching the final week of my stay and I had something I needed to do at the local museum, but I thought it best not to mention the exact nature of my business. I saw the wind disappear from her sails, and we both sat there, gazing at each other like star-crossed lovers, just trying to understand the implications of our predicament. We glanced across at the pond and smiled, just to break the tension. Chris and Henrietta already seemed to have settled into a life of domestic bliss, against all the odds, and we were both envious. Ducks didn't have mortgages, or mobiles; they didn't travel in aeroplanes or get divorced. They just swam around, quacked when the mood took them, laid eggs, had babies and got on with it.

I finished my tea and asked Kura what she wanted to do next, now that our ducks had settled down together.

'Well, the harbour's nice,' she pondered, 'so we could go on a boat trip, maybe check out the gondola and luge rides, take a walk in the park or even hire two bikes, or, what if we went up to my bedroom and made love until it was time to go to the museum? Would that be a good idea?'

I stared straight into her beautiful eyes like a lovesick spaniel.

'Yis!' I croaked.

CHIPTAH 18

In which I finally take Mr Maori home.

Kura woke me up gently at three-thirty p.m., fearful that I would miss my appointment at the museum, which closed at five. I glanced around me at the pretty white room, trying to get my bearings after a long, peaceful sleep. White gossamer-thin curtains floated in the breeze from a large open window that framed the most perfect blue sky I have ever seen. A single, long white cloud hung motionless in the air and all was silent, except for the occasional squawks of the seagulls that floated in and out of the heavenly view.

She knelt on the edge of her bed, gently rubbing my hair. I gazed lazily at her lovely naked brown shoulders, and her perfect breasts, inches from my face. We both knew that this was special. Don't ask me how, but it was genuine love at first sight; that rare phenomenon that strikes so few people in this world. This wasn't just the best love match we could find in our respective postal districts. Somehow, Kura and I had managed to connect with our Global First Choice, in spite of being separated by 12,000 miles. After just two days, we had already discussed homes, marriage and babies. In short, Cupid's magic arrows had done their stuff. Either that or Uncle Ken was busy pulling the strings from up in Heaven.

'You went out like a light after the second time,' Kura smiled, 'so I just popped out to check on Chris and Hen. She's following him around the pond like a dutiful wife already. Listen, we need to get going if you want to visit the museum today. Or I could get back in bed and we could go tomorrow.'

'I wish you hadn't suggested that!' I groaned. 'Like Oscar Wilde, I can resist everything except temptation, but this is extremely important. It's the reason for my trip. I just need to get it out of the way, and then we can relax.'

I quickly dressed and we hopped aboard the Endeavour for the fifteen-minute trip into town. Kura showed me where the car park was and we duly paid and displayed. I grabbed the package containing Mr Maori and dropped the pile of letters into a carrier bag, before locking up and rushing over to the front doors of the museum.

Once inside, I approached the young man on reception, and asked if the manager was in. Instead of answering me, he addressed Kura, who was following up the rear.

'G'day Kura! Are you two together?'

She nodded. 'Yis! Tell the boss I'm here too, would you?'

'Oh, you actually know the manager then?' I asked.

'Yis, I used to work here in my school holidays, until I went to college. Anyway, what's the big secret? Why do you need to see someone from the museum?'

'Ah,' I replied, somewhat nervously. 'I am here on a mission. All will be revealed shortly, my sweet.'

The door from the main museum opened and a striking woman in her mid-to-late fifties entered the reception area. She beamed at her ex employee, and shook hands with me.

'So who do we have here?' she asked.

'This is my new English friend, Adam. He's asked me to bring him here because he needs to see you, and he's being all secretive about it for some reason.'

230

'Not at all,' I laughed, 'but you know what these journalists are like. Just plain nosy! Seriously though, this has been eating away at me for weeks now, and it's quite important. I don't know where to begin.'

'The beginning is good,' suggested Kura. 'Look, I'll leave you two to your business and pop to the ladies' room. I'm disperate! You can fill me in when I get back.'

I waved her off fondly and took a stab at it. 'The thing is, Mrs ..' I began.

'Adam, you can call me Aroha, please!' she insisted.

On hearing this, I almost stopped breathing. It had crossed my mind that she might still be living locally, but I hadn't expected her to be actually running the museum. Flustered, and put off my stride more than somewhat, I abandoned my explanation, handed Aroha the package containing Mr Maori and asked her to open it.

'I have, er, been, erm, asked to return this,' I mumbled, my throat dryer than the bottom of a parrot's cage.

She looked at me quizzically over the rim of her fashionable spectacles and removed the carving from its protective bubble wrap.

'We can give you the money back if you still have the receipt,' she volunteered. 'It's no big deal. Or you can swap it for—'

'No,' I interrupted, 'no, you don't understand. It's a very old and rare Maori carving. Have a closer look.'

'Sorry to disappoint you,' said Aroha, scratching her head, 'but these cost twenty dollars. We have a shelf full of them over there look, all the same. There's a local Maori company been making them for us for nearly forty years. It's just a piece of tourist junk, if I'm honest. Is that the reason you travelled all the way to New Zealand?' she laughed nervously. 'To bring back an unwanted purchase worth twenty dollars? Are you having me on, Adam?'

231

My mind was reeling. I quietly handed Aroha the pile of letters. She took them from me without a word, and just stared at them. After a few seconds spent examining them, I saw tears form in her eyes, and she had to sit down. The young receptionist, realizing all was not well, discreetly vacated the room and left us to it.

'My name is Adam Eve; don't laugh; it was my mother's idea. I didn't know you'd be running this place nowadays. It was quite a shock when I heard your name just now. I recognized it because I read the letters, you see. I'm really sorry to have to tell you that my Uncle Ken has died, and his will dictated that I return the carving to you. I thought you'd like the letters too. I didn't mean to upset you.'

Kura came bursting through the door at this most awkward of moments, and could see immediately that everything wasn't as it should have been.

'What on earth's going on?' she asked. 'Did I miss something vital to the plot? Mom, why are you crying? Adam, what on earth have you just said to her?'

'This lady is your *mother*?' I asked, stunned. My mind felt as if it had suddenly shattered into a hundred pieces as I desperately tried to understand the myriad implications of her words.

'Yis, we were stringing you along, you know, for a laugh, but it seems to have gone pear-shaped all of a sudden. Mom, do you two know each other? What's happened? I need to know.'

'I don't know this young man,' explained Kura's mother, dabbing her eyes with a hankie now, 'but I knew his uncle, thirty-five years ago. Kura, sit down, love. There's something I have to tell you.'

Kura slumped down into a chair and began to chew her nails anxiously. Her soulful eyes darted nervously from Adam to her mother and quickly back again. Her mother continued.

'These are all my letters that I sent him. He was the true love of my life. Do you remember, when you were growing up, I kept saying to you, if you find the one for you, don't let him go, whatever happens? It was because I couldn't bear for you to do what I had done. I obeyed my folks and cast him adrift, just because he wasn't one of us. I regretted that decision all of my life and I never got over it. I often wondered if Ken ever did. I knew your husband was a bad man, and you were too young and naïve to see it for yourself, but *I* couldn't be the one to ban him from your life, after what had happened to me. Ken was the man I wanted and I couldn't have him, so I've been on my own ever since. Now he's dead, so it's all over, but he will always live on, thanks to you.'

Kura frowned as she studied her mother's forlorn, tear-stained face.

'So you're saying …'

'Adam's Uncle Ken was your father, Kura. I'm sorry to spring it on you like this. You were created from our last act of love before I was banned from ever seeing him again. It was all true about you being the result of a doomed love affair. I just never told you who the person was, that's all. I thought it best you didn't try to trace him when you grew up. That would have been just too painful for me to bear.'

'So hang on a minute,' replied Kura, shaking visibly now. 'As if all that wasn't enough of a bombshell, are you also telling me that Adam is my cousin?'

'Jesus Christ!' I blasphemed. I felt as if someone had just pulled a rug from under my feet and cast me down twelve stone steps into a pool full of hungry alligators.

'Mother, Adam and I are in love, this is my new man,' continued Kura, 'he *can't* be my cousin!'

'Adam, are you related to your uncle or your aunt?' asked Kura's mother, clutching at her brow as if a migraine were imminent.

'Erm, my uncle. Oh shit!' I groaned.

'Then Adam is technically your blood cousin. We Maoris can't marry our cousins, Kura,' insisted Aroha.

'Just bloody watch me!' threatened Kura.

The young receptionist arrived with a tea tray and biscuits, only to be sent packing again.

'This is the man I want to be with, mother. I couldn't give a shit if he's technically my bloody blood cousin or not.'

'But think, girl. You've made one big mistake in your life already. Don't make another. I'm sure Adam is lovely – his uncle was, after all – but surely he has his own life in England and you have yours here. There's your first problem for a start, setting aside the legality or advisability of cousins having babies, if you ever chose to start a family.'

'Love will find a way, that's what you always say. We could live half the time here and half the time in England, and who mentioned babies anyway? He has two already; I'll make do with those!'

'Excuse me,' I interrupted. 'Listen, I'm pretty sure it *is* legal to marry your cousin, as it happens. Henry the Eighth changed the rules so he could marry his. Anyway, our relationship wouldn't be frowned upon because no one would even know we were related, apart from you, that is. And as to living half the year here and half the year in England, even that is possible, because I've just inherited a sizeable amount of ... Just a minute. Cancel that.' I slumped into a leather chair, dejected.

'Cancel what?' asked Kura.

'The reason for my trip was to return an important Maori carving that my Uncle Ken stole from the museum on his last evening here, before your grandfather, who I presume is no longer with us, banned him from seeing your mother ever again. He did it in a fit of pique because his world had been turned upside down – a bit like mine has been as it happens. I was supposed to inherit nearly a quarter of a million pounds from his will if I returned the carving and was photographed doing so on the front steps of this museum, by way of proof. Now, I find out that this 'rare' carving he took was nothing more than a piece of tourist shit worth twinty dollars, sorry, twenty dollars, which could well have put paid to my fortune.'

Upon hearing this, suddenly the light of recognition came into Kura's mother's eyes, and she was about to respond, when my mobile rang. I begged her to be patient for a few seconds while I answered it. It was *my* mother, asking if it was convenient to talk. I told her no, but she ploughed on regardless.

'I was just thinking about Len's poo,' she began earnestly. 'I think I was confusing matters by comparing it to rugby posts. Thinking it through, I reckon it was more like an H, which makes H.E. doesn't it? I wonder what that could stand for.'

I thanked her for this latest update, and promised to phone her back at a more convenient time. Unless I was very much mistaken, it was still the middle of the night back in England. Was that really all she had to worry about, I wondered? Then, just as the three of us were about to continue our complex philosophical debate, my mobile rang again, and this time it was Mr Chance, the solicitor, obviously another insomniac.

'Hello, Adam,' he said, a touch sheepishly I thought. 'Are you close to visiting that museum yet?'

I told him that I was already there.

'Ah,' he sighed. 'It's just that, we've had the workmen round at your uncle's flat, getting it tidied up ready for the new occupants to move in, and it appears we've dropped a clanger. One of them has discovered an exquisite old Maori carving in the loft and we thought you should know right away.'

THE END

Japanese tourist taking a photograph
of the inside of a cannon's barrel.

Books in the David Day Series.

A NASTY BUMP ON THE HEAD

Eleven-year-old David Day finds the curmudgeonly toy shop owner, Miss Kettle, murdered in her shop. He duly informs Scotland Yard, only to bump into her in Tenbury Wells the following week.

MONET TROUBLE

First year art student David Day is persuaded to forge a Monet painting by the mysterious Lord Hickman, but unknown to either of them, several other artists have the same idea.

VINCENT GOUGH'S VAN

An art college murder mystery of Shakespearian proportions, littered with psychic sewing teachers, psychotic students and lesbian assassins.

THE CURSE OF TUTTON COMMON

David sets about trying to improve Britain's worst museum, and ably assisted by a cat named Hitlerina, he discovers an ancient Egyptian tomb in South Staffordshire.

PAINTING BY NUMBERS

Thirty-year-old David is having a mid-life crisis, made worse by the fact that his art studio has exploded, and the ninety-year-old 'paint by numbers' enthusiast he has befriended is not what he seems.

STEALING THE ASHES

Forty-year-old David Day overhears two Australian cricketers plotting to steal the Ashes, and, ably hampered by Laz, he tries his best to thwart their plans.

THE HUNT FOR GRANDDAD'S HEAD

The prequel to Nasty Bump! Daleks have invaded Brierley Bank, but David harnesses their power to see off the neighbourhood bully.

Books in the Adam Eve Series.

THE CURIOUS TALE OF THE MISSING HOOF

Writer Adam Eve hires a pantomime horse costume, but forfeits his deposit when he loses one of the hooves. His obsessive efforts to locate it create mayhem!

MR MAORI GOES HOME

Adam Eve's hell-raising uncle has died and left him a substantial amount of money – on condition that he returns a rare Maori carving to New Zealand.

For more information, email gt@geofftristram.co.uk

The David Day and Adam Eve Fan Club

Those of you who have read a David Day or an Adam Eve book will know how addictive they can become. At first, you think you can take them or leave them – you are an adult with a modicum of willpower, after all, and no mere book is going to rule your life. Quite soon though, you realize that you've started reading a quick chapter while you're in the bath or the lavatory. From there it is but a short step to the torch under the bed sheets at midnight and the paperback hidden inside your desk at the office. You'll find yourself reading the final chapter extra slowly to make it last longer, savouring every word and even reading good bits twice. Then, when you can stall no further and the book is finished, you will go through an awful mourning process, whereupon an intense craving will kick in. You'll need more and you'll need it NOW. Bad-tempered due to the crippling withdrawal symptoms, you'll probably complain that the author isn't nearly prolific enough for your voracious appetite, and begin to call him rude names. Extreme cases have even been known to try to climb the walls in anguish. Friends will turn against you because you will insist on regurgitating the plots *ad nauseam* while they're trying to watch television. It will get so bad that you might seriously consider a spell in a rehab clinic, or maybe a course of hypnotism.

Well, help is at hand. Why not join the David Day and Adam Eve Fan Club? It's a bit like Alcoholics Anonymous. You sit around in a circle and confess, 'My name is Deirdre Sponge and I'm a David Day fanatic.' (Obviously, you don't say this if your name *isn't* Deirdre Sponge. That was just an example.) Then the others get up and hug you, with a bit of luck.

If you email me at gt@geofftristram.co.uk, I'll keep your name on file and let you know when a new book is due to be released into the wild. Unlike other authors who are now too important – people such as J.K. Rowling and William Shakespeare for example – I promise to be approachable, grateful, humble, and always write back. That's with the proviso that you tell me my books are great, of course. I don't want any sour-faced old scrooges writing in to tell me I'm rubbish and that I deserve to be horse-whipped on the steps of my fan club. Maybe I could cope if you'd spotted a glaring error, or a bit you didn't think made perfect sense, but obviously, I'd prefer it if you told me how a paragraph had made you wet yourself on the train, or prevented you from leaping off a high building to certain death. You can suggest things that David or Adam can get up to in future stories, if you wish. I might even write *you* into a book. After all, most of my characters are based on real people, believe it or not! Oops! Shouldn't have admitted that – now no one will believe that legal disclaimer in the small print at the beginning.

Anyway, I'll leave it with you. The offer's there. You can lead a horse to water but you can't make it drink, as my Granny Bertha often attempted to say. I hope you've enjoyed *Mr Maori Goes Home*. If it didn't make you laugh, I'll refund your money.

That was a joke by the way. You have to be so careful in this litigious age. I need the money for a new conservatory – I can't afford to give it back. The bookshops keep forty per cent anyway. And another thing. Will you stop lending my books to everyone when you've finished them? Let them buy their own. I'm never going to be another J.K. Rowling at this rate.

Geoff Tristram

'Adam, it's your mother here again. Listen, I've been thinking. Could it stand for Happy Ending, do you think?'